LIFE NATURE LIBRARY

# THE
# REPTILES

*Other Publications:*

LIFE NATURE LIBRARY

# THE REPTILES

by Archie Carr
and the Editors of
TIME-LIFE BOOKS

*Revised Edition*

TIME-LIFE BOOKS / ALEXANDRIA, VIRGINIA

**ON THE COVER:** In a head-on view, a deadly bamboo viper from
Taiwan glistens like polished jade. The deep pits between the
red eyes are heat-sensing organs that assist this poisonous reptile to
search out and strike its warm-blooded prey.

# Contents

Time-Life Books Inc.
is a wholly owned subsidiary of
TIME INCORPORATED

FOUNDER: Henry R. Luce 1898-1967

*Editor-in-Chief:* Henry Anatole Grunwald
*Chairman of the Board:* Andrew Heiskell
*President:* James R. Shepley
*Editorial Director:* Ralph Graves
*Vice Chairman:* Arthur Temple

TIME-LIFE BOOKS INC.
MANAGING EDITOR: Jerry Korn
*Executive Editor:* David Maness
*Assistant Managing Editors:* Dale M. Brown (planning),
George Constable, Jim Hicks (acting),
Martin Mann, John Paul Porter
*Art Director:* Tom Suzuki
*Chief of Research:* David L. Harrison
*Director of Photography:* Robert G. Mason
*Senior Text Editor:* Diana Hirsh
*Assistant Art Director:* Arnold C. Holeywell
*Assistant Chief of Research:* Carolyn L. Sackett
*Assistant Director of Photography:* Dolores A. Littles

CHAIRMAN: Joan D. Manley
*President:* John D. McSweeney
*Executive Vice Presidents:* Carl G. Jaeger,
John Steven Maxwell, David J. Walsh
*Vice Presidents:* Peter G. Barnes (comptroller),
Nicholas Benton (public relations), John L. Canova (sales),
Nicholas J. C. Ingleton (Asia), James L. Mercer
(Europe/South Pacific), Herbert Sorkin
(production), Paul R. Stewart (promotion)
*Personnel Director:* Beatrice T. Dobie
*Consumer Affairs Director:* Carol Flaumenhaft

LIFE NATURE LIBRARY
STAFF FOR THE FIRST EDITION
EDITOR: Maitland A. Edey
*Assistant to the Editor:* John Purcell
*Copy Editor:* Percy Knauth
*Designer:* Paul Jensen
*Staff Writers:* David Bergamini, Robert McClung,
Peter Meyerson
*Chief Researcher:* Martha T. Goolrick
*Researchers:* Gerald A. Bair, David Beckwith, Doris Bry,
Robert Cowen, Susan Freudenheim, LeClair G. Lambert,
Paula Norworth, Susan Rayfield, Phyllis M. Williamson

STAFF FOR THE REVISED EDITION
EDITOR: Patricia Hunt
*Text Editor:* Sterling Seagrave
*Staff Writers:* Dalton Delan, Abigail Zuger
*Researcher:* Carol Forsyth Mickey

EDITORIAL PRODUCTION
*Production Editor:* Douglas B. Graham
*Operations Manager:* Gennaro C. Esposito,
Gordon E. Buck (assistant)
*Assistant Production Editor:* Feliciano Madrid
*Quality Control:* Robert L. Young (director),
James J. Cox (assistant), Michael G. Wight (associate)
*Art Coordinator:* Anne B. Landry
*Copy Staff:* Susan B. Galloway (chief), Margery duMond,
Florence Keith, Celia Beattie
*Picture Department:* Cathy Doxat-Pratt
*Traffic:* Jeanne Potter

The following individuals of Time Inc. were helpful in
producing the book: LIFE staff photographers Larry Burrows,
Alfred Eisenstaedt, Eliot Elisofon, Fritz Goro, Nina Leen

CORRESPONDENTS: Elisabeth Kraemer (Bonn); Margot
Hapgood, Dorothy Bacon (London); Susan Jonas,
Lucy T. Voulgaris (New York); Maria Vincenza Aloisi,
Josephine du Brusle (Paris); Ann Natanson (Rome).
Valuable assistance was also provided by Carolyn T. Chubet,
Miriam Hsia (New York)

## About the Author

Archie Carr, though born in Mobile, Alabama, has long been as much a part of Florida as the reptiles there he knows and loves so well. He went to college at the University of Florida, received his M.S. and his Ph.D. there and has taught in the biology department of that institution since 1937. Fascinated by turtles and snakes from the time he was a boy, he is known far beyond the boundaries of Florida as probably the greatest authority on sea turtles in the world. He is particularly identified with the Caribbean Conservation Corporation, an organization dedicated to saving the green turtle from extinction, and has directed a seasonal research program at the breeding ground of the green turtle at Tortuguero, Costa Rica. He has also worked extensively on other continents, notably Africa, Australia and South America. A prolific writer as well as a scientist, he is the author of numerous scientific papers and 11 books, including *The Everglades* in The American Wilderness series. For two of these books he won the Daniel Giraud Elliott medal for preeminence in zoology, and the John Burroughs medal for nature writing. In 1973 the World Wildlife Fund awarded him its gold medal for the application of scientific findings to the conservation of marine turtles; most recently, he received the Edward W. Browning Award for achievement in biological conservation.

# 1

# The "Cold-Blooded" Fraternity

THE reactions of the little girl on the opposite page epitomize the feelings of people generally about reptiles. Most people have a vague feeling that no reptiles except turtles are to be trusted, and so make no effort to find out anything about them or even to learn what they are. It would scarcely be necessary in writing a book about birds, say, to make sure at the outset that the reader knew what birds were, but in the case of reptiles this is sadly true. Therefore one should start with a definition that excludes frogs, toads, platypuses, mudskippers, armadillos and a good many other odd animals which are constantly being mistakenly lumped with reptiles.

A proper reptile, to begin with, is a vertebrate animal. It has scales, breathes air (not water), characteristically lays shelled eggs and depends on outside sources for its body heat. There are in the world only five main groups of animals that fit this definition. They are the turtles, the lizards, the snakes, the crocodilians, and a strange, little-seen creature called the tuatara, which looks like a lizard but is not. In these latest days of geologic history, there are about 6,000 species of reptiles scattered over the earth. Though they are most diverse and numerous in warm regions, they range far northward too, turning up in

## THE ABUNDANCE OF REPTILES TODAY

LIZARDS
3,000 species

SNAKES
2,700 species

TURTLES
220 species

CROCODILIANS
21 species

TUATARA
1 species

*Of the 16 orders of reptiles known from fossils, only four have managed to survive until modern times. The largest by far, the Squamata, combines both lizards and snakes, with a grand total of about 5,700 living species. By contrast, there are only 220 species of turtles and 21 species of crocodilians throughout the world, and the tuatara alone in New Zealand. The last two were not always so scarce. Fossils of at least 108 species of extinct crocodilians are known. And the rhynchocephalian order, to which the tuatara belongs, has numbered at least 23 species.*

the yards of rural Swedes, Siberians and citizens of the state of Maine. They even occur on the dusty deserts of the world.

It so happens that I live in Florida, which is one of the good reptile regions. I have a farm with woods around it and a marshy pond out front. The place offers a fine sampling of the main groups of reptiles. The farm is no Cretaceous swamp, but through the years we have caught, seen, stepped on or had the house invaded by a great many different kinds of reptiles, representing all the main groups except the tuatara.

To begin with, the farm is extraordinarily blessed with turtles, and a stroll around it gives a broad impression of turtle build and customs. The turtles there are both aquatic and terrestrial. They spread in size from the four-inch (10.2-cm) stinkjims to snappers that weigh 30 pounds (13.6 kg) or more and in disposition from the long-necked, short-tempered, carnivorous soft-shells that lurk on the pond bottom snorkeling air through tubular nostrils to the various placid, dome-shelled water turtles, called cooters in Florida, which bask on logs, forage for edible trash on the bottom or cruise about chomping at fallen cow-crazy petals floating on the water. Industrious gopher turtles follow their small trails out from vaulted burrows and graze among the grazing cows. Once in a long while a box turtle comes meditating through the yard and retires to its shell until we go away. The box turtle seems to me the spiritual essence of turtle mildness and conservatism.

In calling turtles conservative I have mainly in mind their sticking to an ancestral architecture devised a very long time ago—certainly not the architecture itself, which is about the most bizarre modification of vertebrate structure ever made. For the specialty of turtles is armor, a shell made up of a top part (the carapace) and a belly part (the plastron). The two parts are generally joined at each side by a bony bridge. Top and bottom, the shell has two layers, an outer one made up of broad, horny scales joined by stout seams and an inner, usually much thicker layer of tightly jointed bones. Because the seams do not coincide, the structure forms an extremely strong casing within which much, and in some cases all, of the turtle can be safely stowed away.

THE origin of this shell has not been convincingly revealed by paleontologists, and so it is not possible to say just where in the reptile record the turtle line begins. A little reptile called Eunotosaurus that lived some 250 million years ago in the Permian age is often pointed to as a probable turtle ancestor. It had ribs which were broadened in a way that suggests a rudimentary shell. But whatever the beginnings of turtles may have been, the shell is now the mark of the creature. In spite of the millions of years of evolution that have seen turtles established nearly everywhere on the earth except in the air, the shell, in some readily recognizable form, has been retained.

The advantage the shell brought must have been strong, because it is not an easy thing to live with. Embryologically, it is a sort of nightmare. To live in it and keep their front legs working right, turtles had to rearrange their shoulder girdle, bringing it back into an unprecedented position inside the rib case. This is not a thing that happened once back in the Permian and then was done forever. Each time an embryo becomes a turtle it happens all over again, just as each baby flounder is first an upright fish with an eye properly on either side, and then later becomes flattened, with both eyes on the same side.

The shell has also dictated a change in the method of breathing. Because a turtle cannot expand its chest at all, it must suck in air by moving things about inside. By contracting a pair of muscles back at the flanks the turtle can increase the volume of the space around the lungs, and the air rushes in. To expel air, it contracts another set of muscles under the viscera, pushing the internal organs forward to squeeze against the lungs. A number of other physiological adjustments makes breathing a distinctive process in turtles and, incidentally, one about which a great deal remains to be learned.

Turtles range in weight from a few ounces to well over half a ton (454 kg). The biggest turtles are aquatic, but there are big ones on land too. The famous Galápagos tortoises, and others on islands in the Indian Ocean, have reached weights of over 400 pounds (181 kg). During the Pleistocene, there were even bigger ones in various parts of the world.

THERE is a popular notion that turtles live, as it were, forever. Little is known scientifically about their maximum life span, however, and it is not possible to evaluate this notion. Careful sifting of records from zoos, and of the generally shaky evidence afforded by turtles with dates carved into their shells, has led some herpetologists, as students of reptiles are called, to suggest a figure of a hundred years as a probable maximum. Few turtles living near man realize this potentiality. They get run over on the road, their marshes or ponds are drained, their streams are poisoned, or they are simply caught and eaten. Fortunately for their survival, their longevity does not mean they are slow to mature. In fact, turtles reach sexual maturity in a surprisingly short time. In the several species for which data are available, including some of the big sea turtles, breeding may begin at ages of from three to eight years.

The most distinctive of living turtles is the giant leatherback sea turtle. Though it looks like a turtle, it has no proper turtle shell, but only a rubbery skin covering a mosaic of little, pebble-like bones which have nothing to do with the broad bones of the ordinary turtle carapace and are not connected to the skeleton at all. While the four other genera of sea turtles show some modification of the bony carapace, their shells are more like those of land and freshwater turtles. Another turtle group that stands apart is that of the soft-shelled, or pancake, turtles, distributed in Africa, Asia and North America. In these the horny shell is also replaced by a continuous skin, and the edge is thin, floppy cartilage with no supporting marginal bones.

The motley array of the remaining kinds of turtles falls into two main groups, according to the way they draw in their necks. Most of them, the Cryptodira (hidden necks), retire with the neck bent into a vertically folding, S-shaped curve. They are found in Europe, Asia, Africa and the Americas. The other group, the side-necked turtles (Pleurodira), brings the neck in sideways and lays it along the body under the fore eaves of the shell. Side-necks are confined to tropics of the southern continents, Africa, South America and Australia. One of them is the famous matamata *(Chelys fimbriata)*, the most grotesque-looking of all the turtles. The matamata, in fact, does not look like a turtle at all; it looks like a pile of leaves. In Colombia, where it is commonly found lying neck-deep in the water of swampy streams, homely people are sometimes referred to as having *cara de matamata*, the features of a matamata. I judge that this is not said to their faces.

From the standpoint of abundance and diversity, the lizards and snakes are by far the most flourishing reptiles of today. Between them the two groups include about 750 genera and at least 5,700 species. They occur on every continent except Antarctica. Snakes are clearly derived from some ancient kind of

## STRUCTURAL TROUBLES OF TURTLES

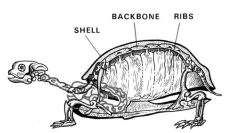

*The internal rearrangements that turtles have to put up with in order to live inside a hard shell are drastic. In the hidden-neck group the backbone has become fused to the shell. Its ribs are flattened and widened like fence palings to ensure maximum support. Its shoulder blades and hips are inside what would be the chest of a more conventional vertebrate. Its long and flexible neck can be retracted in an S curve, pulling the head inside the shell for safety.*

## HOW LIZARDS DIFFER FROM SNAKES

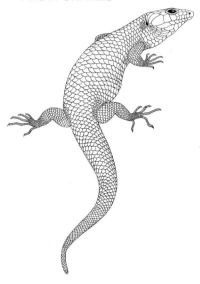

*Although lizards and snakes belong to the same reptilian order, they have clearly visible differences. A typical lizard moves about on four limbs. It hears air-borne sounds through external ear openings, and sees with an eye that may be covered by two movable eyelids. The typical snake, on the other hand, moves by undulating its body and is aided by broad ventral scales that catch against the ground and keep it from slithering backward. It hears through its skull bones, which transmit vibrations from the ground. A transparent glassy scale covers its unwinking eye.*

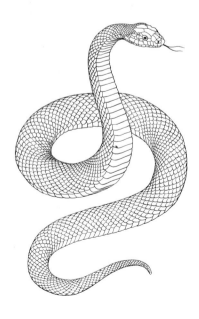

lizard, and the two are put together in the reptilian order of Squamata. One of the features distinguishing the lizards and snakes from other reptiles is a drastic reduction of bones in the temporal region of the skull, which reaches its extreme among the snakes. Another is that the anal opening in lizards and snakes is transverse, instead of longitudinal as in crocodilians and turtles. Finally, both snakes and lizards have paired copulatory organs, and both have distinctive sets of sensory cells in their mouths, called Jacobson's organs.

As to differences between snakes and lizards themselves, most lizards can close their eyes, but a snake's eyes remain permanently open behind a clear covering called the spectacle. The unblinking stare of snakes may account for some of the superstitious fears people have about them. Snakes also generally have a single row of widened scales under the belly, while the scales of lizards tend to be more nearly the same size above and below. Lizards typically have some sort of external ear; snakes have none. In most lizards the tail can be readily shed, evidently as an escape mechanism. In some, the broken-off section snaps and jumps about in an irresponsible way. It is easy to imagine that this allows the rest of the lizard to slip quietly away from the scene while its attacker is preoccupied with the twitching tail. Later, a new tail generally grows again, sometimes lighter in color, with a different scale pattern and shorter than the one that was left behind.

The most obvious difference between typical lizards and snakes, however, is the leglessness of the latter. Although there are lizards that have no legs and that superficially resemble snakes, it is still generally easy to draw the line between the two groups. At the same time, it also is helpful to keep in mind that snakes are really a specialized and quite successful sort of lizard.

Of the two groups of the Squamata, the lizards are of course the older. They have the conventional body plan of a typical land vertebrate: four legs, five toes to a foot, and the sprawling gait of the earliest reptiles. Most of the adaptations that have allowed them to spread and prosper are relatively unspectacular changes in the old four-legged look—exceptions being the various groups in which the legs have been lost completely. As vertebrates, lizards are a fairly representative group and it has been suggested that the lizard would be more suitable as a type with which to introduce freshman biology students to vertebrate anatomy than the universally used frog. Perhaps it sounds cynical to say so, but I think the answer there is that the frog, being tailless, fits dissection pans more gracefully.

In spite of their fundamentally conventional body plan, modern lizards are a diverse lot. They range in length from two inches (5.1 cm) to 10 feet (3 m). They may look like dragons or like worms, and they show a complex adaptive range through terrestrial, arboreal, subterraneous and aquatic environments.

Out at my farm lizards are all over the place on warm days. The large family of the Iguanidae is there, represented by the slender anole that stalks insects on the screens, and by the scaly-backed fence lizards that bask on almost every log or stump. This is, as the name suggests, the group to which the big tropical arboreal and marine iguanas belong, and it includes a host of smaller forms. Its counterpart in the Old World is the family Agamidae, which has a curiously similar structural and ecological spread.

The classic lizards—classic because they are of the Old World and since early times have beguiled European naturalists—are the personable lacertas of the family Lacertidae. My farm is, of course, devoid of lacertas, and this is a shame. Their place is partly taken by the athletic, silky skinned, six-lined race-runner, *Cnemidophorus*, a member of the related family Teiidae. The teiids are an alert and active lot of lizards that mostly occur in South America but are also found foraging about dooryards among chickens and babies in villages throughout the Caribbean. At the farm the racerunner streaks across the paths, and in summer the hot, bare sand in all the open places is slashed with its tracks.

The most cosmopolitan lizard family is that of the skinks, the Scincidae—shiny-scaled lizards with protrusible tongues and a generally surreptitious air, which may account for their being occasionally known as scorpions. One of the farm skinks, the ground lizard, is a brown slip not much bigger than an old wooden match. The other is the big, burnished redheaded scorpion, which irks squirrel hunters with the noise it makes skittering up the trunks of trees.

A DAY of plowing or harrowing is likely to turn up two kinds of lizards that have no legs. One is the so-called glass snake, which dashes headlong into the soil and makes one wonder why a European relative is known as the slowworm. The other is the Florida worm lizard, a blind, pink, double-ended creature like a blunt night-crawler worm. The worm-lizard family is called Amphisbaenidae, literally meaning "to walk on both ends," because among most of the creatures in it both ends look surprisingly alike. As these two burrowers show, snakes were not the only legless descendants of the ancestral lizard stocks. Through the world list of lizard families, legless members repeatedly turn up, a drastic adaptation that seems odd to a beast as dependent on his legs as man.

The giants among modern lizards are the monitors (family Varanidae), which are believed to be close to the ancestral line from which snakes came. In the East Indies, there is a monitor aptly if over-sensationally known as the Komodo dragon that is longer than 10 feet (3 m), and there are African and Asian species that by far exceed the average size for modern lizards. Monitors are fierce predators which run down and rend quite large prey. They have long, flexible necks, protrusible tongues like snakes, and an intense way of looking at people that makes them feel uneasy.

There are no monitors on the farm, nor indeed are there any wild ones anywhere in the Western Hemisphere. There are no real chameleons out there either, or any Gila monsters. But the greatest deprivation we suffer is the lack of geckos. To residents of the tropics all over the world, the geckos—lizards of the family Gekkonidae—are a familiar institution. Geckos have many features that endear them to the open-minded. They live trustingly in people's houses. They have loose skins, vertical pupils, no eyelids and a voice—the only voice among lizards and one of the few really reliable voices in the whole class of reptiles. The name gecko is an effort at onomatopoeia, being suggestive of the sounds made by an Old World species known technically (and a bit redundantly) as *Gekko gecko*. A South African gecko, *Ptneopus garrulus*, gets its specific name from the habit of calling vociferously from the mouths of burrows that it makes on hillsides. Almost everybody who knows geckos is fond of them. Even people who mistakenly believe they are poisonous seem secretly pleased to have them around. The herpetologist Clifford Pope spoke of their magnetism and suggested that they may surpass baby turtles as potential pets. I agree, with but one reservation: A child is apt to be horrified when a gecko reacts to having its tail pulled by simply dropping off the tail into the child's hand.

We come now to the snakes, and it is interesting, in the light of their close relationship to, and derivation from, lizards, that some of the most primitive

## A DISPOSABLE TAIL

*At the touch of a badger, a fence lizard gives its hungry foe the slip by dropping its tail. This disconcerting defense is used by many lizards. The spot where the tail can break off is preset by a crack in a vertebra, and the muscles nearby are also arranged so they will separate neatly. As if this sudden splitting of one succulent morsel into two were not enough, the predator's momentary confusion is increased by the lively twisting and turning of the severed tail, while the little lizard darts off in safety to grow a new one.*

living snakes are burrowers whose skeletons retain traces of the old limb girdles from ancient lizard times. One family, the worm snakes (family Typhlopidae), is made up of tiny species with much reduced eyes and teeth, blunt heads, little scales and even the remnants of a pelvis. They have some features that have led some experts to suggest that they are not snakes at all, but are actually considered to be aberrant lizards.

Much better known, more conspicuous and far more numerous are the four principal snake families, the Boidae, the Colubridae, the Viperidae and the Elapidae. The first of these, and the most primitive, includes the New World boas and anacondas, and the pythons of the Old World tropics. They are constrictors: They kill their prey by wrapping themselves around it and squeezing. Although there are some small members of the group, the Boidae as a family are notorious for being the largest snakes in the world. There are well-authenticated records of anacondas more than 37 feet (11.3 m) long, pythons of 33 feet (10.1 m), boa constrictors of 18 feet (5.5 m). Generally speaking, pythons and boas resemble each other closely, but the former lay eggs and the latter bear live young. There are also slight skeletal differences between them.

THE second major snake family, the Colubridae, is by far the most diversified. It contains about two thirds of the world's snakes which, for want of a better name, go under the general heading of "typical" snakes. There are colubrids wherever snakes are found. As might be expected, they are the most numerous and varied snakes on my Florida farm. Within a hundred yards (91 m) of the house you can find snakes to show the main colubrid habits and habitats. Down at the pond edge, for instance, if you go to see why a frog is screaming, you will probably find that a water snake—a banded or green water snake—has hold of it, or perhaps a common garter snake. Or if it is a tiny, thin scream it may be that a ribbon snake is trying to swallow a gangling tree frog. The most ubiquitous snakes on the place are the black snake and the rat snake, or chicken snake. The two belong to different but related groups with worldwide distribution. The chicken snake is an *Elaphe*, a slow-moving, mainly arboreal constrictor, most readily found by joining any conclave of irate blue jays. The black snake belongs to the genus *Coluber*, which, with the whip snakes, includes some of the most agile and enterprising snakes in the world.

The farm colubrids range from a scarce red-bellied *Storeria* that creeps about in leaf mold and matures at a length of five inches (12.7 cm) to the handsome gun-metal indigo snake that can swallow a rabbit. The rear-fang contingent—the typical snakes that have independently hit upon poison as a device to get food—is represented by the crown snake, *Tantilla*, which has grooved fangs but is too small to get a grip on a human. You can dig up a scarlet snake a foot (30 cm) underground, or chase a coachwhip over many acres, or see a slender twig on a bush turn into the air-thin grace of *Opheodrys*, the rough green snake. Most of the typical snakes on the place lay eggs, but some bear their young alive. Some eat any living prey they can catch and swallow, but the hog-nosed snakes lean heavily on toads for food, the king snake eats other snakes, and the red-bellied mud snake in the pond eats mostly salamanders.

The remaining snakes of the farm and of the world constitute two groups among which the production and injection of venom have become highly refined adaptations. These are the vipers and the cobras, the latter group including the coral snakes. The cobras and their relatives (family Elapidae) are found around the world in tropical regions. They kill prey by venom injected through fixed hollow or grooved fangs located toward the front of the upper jaw. They are generally slender as compared with vipers, and except for one Australian species their heads are not markedly broadened or heart-shaped. Some of them, like the mambas of Africa, are big, swift, obstreperous and even warlike. Others are timid burrowers or foragers in leaf mold, like most of the American coral snakes. The king cobra of India with its frightening hood reaches a top length of about 18 feet (5.5 m), but some of the burrowing elapids may be only a few centimeters long, with a gape of mouth too narrow for biting people. In Australia, the cobra-like snakes by far outnumber the typical snakes. There is a fantastic variety of species there, including such creatures as the dreaded tiger snake, the death adder and the 12-foot (3.7-m) taipan, perhaps the most ferocious snake in the world when provoked.

THE poisonous snakes with the most elaborate venom-injection apparatus are the vipers (family Viperidae). They are found on all the continents except Australia; in fact, most poisonous snakes of temperate regions are vipers. There are two well-marked groups of them: the true vipers (subfamily Viperinae), confined to the Old World; and the pit vipers (subfamily Crotalinae), which have both American and Asiatic members but are mainly concentrated in the New World. Most vipers are stout-bodied snakes with the wedge-shaped or heart-shaped head generally thought of as the mark of a poisonous snake. The pit vipers include such imposing animals as the rattlesnakes and the tropical American fer-de-lance and bushmaster. Their name is derived from a sensory depression, or pit, in the side of the snout between the eye and the nostril. This is elaborately supplied with nerves and blood vessels and is an organ specialized for detecting the presence and range of warm objects. Most pit vipers eat warm-blooded prey, and the pit is no doubt used primarily in feeding, but like the rattle of the rattlesnake it is perhaps also of value as a means of avoiding injury under the hoofs of big mammals.

The only way my farm stands out in the serpent-rich north Florida landscape is in the prevalence of poisonous snakes there. A coral snake on the lawn

### A GIANT SCAVENGER

*The Komodo dragon named for the East Indian island where it was first found, is the largest living lizard. A voracious and undiscriminating carnivore, it will eat any kind of carrion, as well as living animals. Lethargic when it has fed, this monitor lizard shows surprising spurts of speed when hungry, and uses its long, strong tail with lethal dexterity.*

is no great event at all. Cottonmouth moccasins come up from the pond—every now and then the cook kills one at the kitchen door. Diamondback rattlesnakes are abundant, and pygmy rattlers turn up occasionally underfoot. In fact, a snake found in the yard is almost if not quite as likely to be venomous as harmless, and this is by no means the case in most places.

We have had five children ranging the premises for a dozen years and they have to date remained unbitten. The only friction we have had with snakes has been their killing of our dogs. A series of low-slung dogs has lived on the place—trustful bassets, and testy dachshunds opposed to all forms of life not canine or human. Of these canine companions of ours, three, and perhaps four, have been killed by snakes.

LIKE any proper Florida pond, ours has an alligator in it. Alligators belong to the order Crocodilia, the third major group of reptiles, which includes three living families. One of these, the Alligatoridae, has in it the familiar American alligator, its close relative the Chinese alligator and the various tropical American caimans. The second family is the Crocodylidae, the true crocodiles, dwarf crocodiles and the false gavial. The third, the Gavialidae, has a single living representative, the slim-jawed, fish-eating gavial of southern Asia, a fierce-looking but timid creature.

Crocodilia are in some respects the most advanced of reptiles. They share with higher vertebrates a four-chambered heart. This makes possible a more efficient circulation than other reptiles have, because in the usual reptilian three-chambered heart there is some mixing of newly oxygenated blood from the lungs with the deoxygenated blood just in from the tissues of the body. Another advanced feature of crocodilians is a partition between the cavities of the chest and abdomen that suggests the diaphragm of mammals. In crocodilians the cloacal opening is a longitudinal slit as in turtles, instead of being transverse as in lizards and snakes.

Full-grown crocodilians range in size from between three and four feet (0.9 to 1.2 m), in the case of the Congo dwarf crocodile and the dwarf caiman, to top lengths of over 20 feet (6.1 m) in the salt-water crocodiles. The biggest American alligator ever measured was slightly over 19 feet (5.8 m) long. How long crocodilians live is not certain, although they have long been thought of as practically indestructible creatures that live forever. In the rare places in which they are not killed long before that by man they probably do reach ages of 50 years or more. They appear to mature at an age of eight to 10 years.

Crocodilians have one of the few well-developed voices among reptiles. In its timbre and impact on the surroundings, the voice of the American alligator must be considered one of the great animal voices of the world. It is a matter of family pride that the alligator which nearly a decade ago appeared at a tender age in our pond finally began to sing. For six years he had cruised silently about, methodically eating or driving off other alligators that came in from other places, and cracking mud turtles with a ghastly noise that disgusted my daughter. Then one misty morning he came forth with the earth-shaking, soul-stirring song of his kind. I suppose this means he is growing up. Or she—the females bellow too.

The remaining order of living reptiles, the Rhynchocephalia, has one living representative. This is the tuatara, *Sphenodon punctatus*. There are no tuataras on our farm. They live only on a few islands off the coast of New Zealand, and their story will be told in a later chapter.

TOKAY GECKO, A FOOT-LONG (30-CM) LIZARD OF ASIA, IS ONE OF THE FEW REPTILES TO LIVE WITH MAN—IT IS AN ADEPT INSECT CATCHER

# The Venerable Reptiles

Once the dominant form of life on earth, the reptiles are now vastly reduced in numbers and variety. They persist today in three main groups—the turtles, the lizards and snakes, and the crocodilians—plus one almost extinct form, the little-known tuatara. Many are relatively unchanged from the age when dinosaurs rumbled over the land, and offer fascinating hints as to what life was like then.

# The Anatomy of a Reptile

Although no single reptile can be considered typical of all reptiles, the alligator is as good a representative as any, since it has a backbone, is cold-blooded, lays eggs with shells and has a reptilian skin—i.e., either slated, scaled or shell-like. Nevertheless it has advanced features which are peculiar to it. Its four-chambered heart is more efficient than the three-chambered hearts of other reptiles, which tend to mix freshly oxygenated blood with unoxygenated

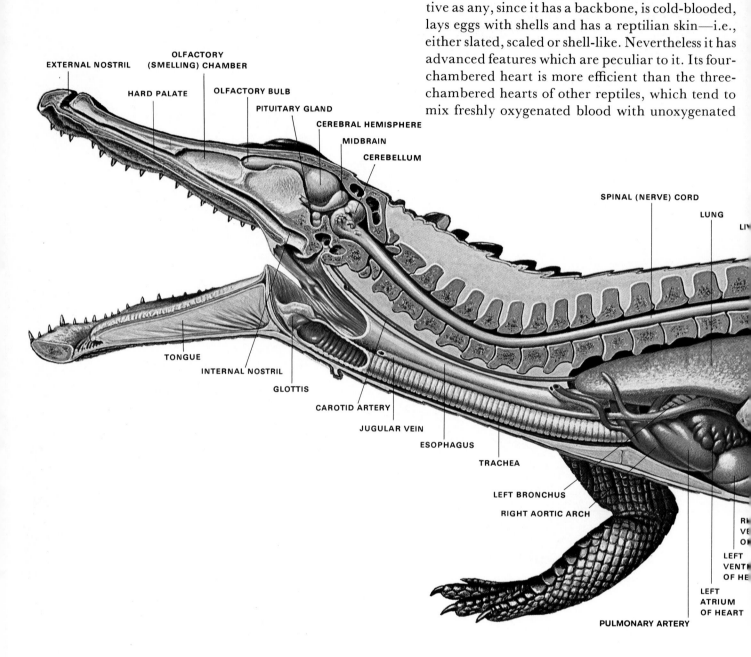

EXTERNAL NOSTRIL
OLFACTORY (SMELLING) CHAMBER
HARD PALATE
OLFACTORY BULB
PITUITARY GLAND
CEREBRAL HEMISPHERE
MIDBRAIN
CEREBELLUM
SPINAL (NERVE) CORD
LUNG
LI
TONGUE
INTERNAL NOSTRIL
GLOTTIS
CAROTID ARTERY
JUGULAR VEIN
ESOPHAGUS
TRACHEA
LEFT BRONCHUS
RIGHT AORTIC ARCH
R
VE
O
LEFT VENT OF HE
LEFT ATRIUM OF HEART
PULMONARY ARTERY

**MOUTH.** To achieve its characteristic gape, the alligator does not merely drop its lower jaw but raises its head and upper jaw. The teeth are used for seizing and holding prey—not chewing.

**STOMACH.** Because an alligator cannot chew, its stomach has two parts—a muscular gizzard and a digestive section. The gizzard's grinding of food is aided by swallowing hard objects.

**HEART.** Blood passes from the right ventricle through the pulmonary artery for oxygenation by the lungs; it returns through the left atrium to left ventricle, and is pumped out to the body.

**SCALES.** The alligator's armor is composed of horny scales, each developing on its own and replaced by layers from below. Those shielding the back and tail have bony plates beneath them.

blood. Its respiratory system is better. The nostrils are separated from the mouth by a hard palate. When the alligator swallows a struggling victim there is no danger that a desperate kick will penetrate the roof of its mouth and damage its brain. The alligator has well-developed lungs in comparison to the more primitive saclike structure of snakes. It has the most highly developed brain of any reptile, and is one of the few to have its teeth firmly set in its jaws.

On the other hand, the alligator lacks a well-developed Jacobson's organ, which means that its ability to detect tastes and odors is not nearly so acute as a snake's. It has the well-developed digestive system which works so efficiently for all reptiles, but lacks a bladder, although most turtles and lizards have one. Its ammoniac kidney wastes, along with intestinal wastes, pass through a chamber called the cloaca which opens to the outside of the body.

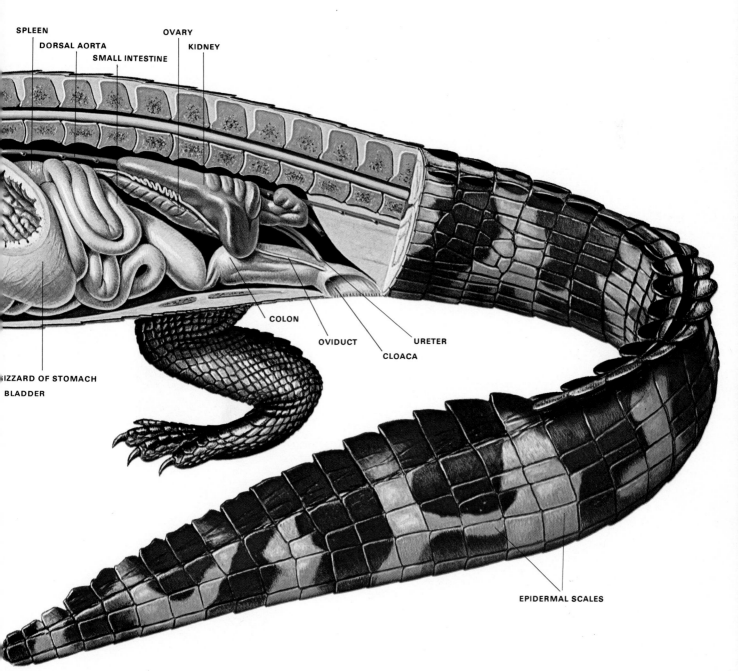

SPLEEN
DORSAL AORTA
SMALL INTESTINE
OVARY
KIDNEY
COLON
OVIDUCT
URETER
CLOACA
GIZZARD OF STOMACH
BLADDER
EPIDERMAL SCALES

# The Tenacious Turtles

Clumsy object that it is, the shell has helped ensure the survival of the turtles for 175 million years. Today it is still worn by all species, although it has been modified to suit a variety of environments. Sea turtles, for example, have jettisoned much of their shell bone and are among the fastest-moving of modern reptiles. Land turtles have thinned theirs down to make tiptoe locomotion on their elephantine feet less ponderous. Soft-shelled turtles, which live in fresh water, have developed pancake-shaped shells with flexible edges which they use to help bury themselves. Lying hidden in shallow water, waiting for prey, they occasionally crane their long necks to breathe air with their snorkel-like nostrils. Sometimes they remain submerged for several hours, extracting sufficient oxygen from the water they pump in and out of their pharynges. Recent studies have revealed that turtles can survive for long periods without taking in any oxygen from the outside.

Turtles are believed to be quite hard of hearing. Although they have well-developed middle and inner ears, and although some have voices, the latest evidence is that they hear only sounds of low frequency. They rely instead on their skins and shells to pick up vibrations from the ground or water. They can live a year or more without eating. Some females, in the most amazing feat of all, can produce fertilized eggs as long as five years after mating.

THE DESERT TORTOISE, found in the American Southwest, is protected against loss of moisture by its shell and uses its burrow less as a retreat from danger than as a place to cool off.

THE SPINELESS SOFT-SHELLED TURTLE of the central and southwestern U.S. can hide in the beds of rivers, streams and ponds by shuffling its leathery-skinned shell into sand or silt.

A HAWKSBILL AND A GREEN TURTLE, dwelling in the warm seas, show aquatic adaptations—lightweight shells and paddle-like legs. They swim with birdlike flaps of their front flippers.

21

THE GAVIAL OF INDIA, WITH A RECORDED MAXIMUM LENGTH OF 21.5 FEET (6.6 M), HAS THE NARROWEST SNOUT OF ANY CROCODILIAN

THE NILE CROCODILE, one of the largest of the crocodilians, grows 20 feet (6.1 m) long. The adult feeds on fishes, mammals and other reptiles—even its young—and is a noted man-killer.

# The Hulking Crocodilians

The crocodilians—the heavily armored crocodiles, alligators and gavials—are the largest of the modern reptiles and the last surviving reptilian descendants of the stock that also produced the dinosaurs. Although somewhat clumsy out of water, they are superbly equipped for living in it. They are strong swimmers, and experts at drifting along on the surface, submerged except for their bulging eyes and nostrils, their long flat jaws not even making a ripple in the water as they stalk turtles, swimming birds and fishes. The larger crocodiles can sometimes get close enough to animals on shore to sweep them—and humans—into deep water with their tails. Crocodilians have valves in their ears and nostrils to keep water out. Because their mouths lack lips and thus do not shut completely, two palatal flaps cover gullet and windpipe during dives.

AND USES IT TO SIDESWIPE FISHES. DESPITE ITS FIERCE LOOK, IT IS A TIMID ANIMAL AND USUALLY RETREATS AT THE SIGHT OF MAN

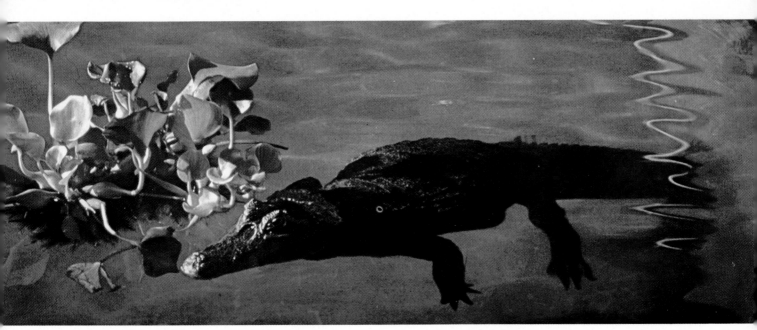

**THE SOUTH AMERICAN CAIMAN,** a 6- to 10-foot (1.8- to 3-m) relative of the mild-mannered American alligator, is considered to be a fierce biter, and even as a hatchling it will bare its teeth.

It is the noisiest crocodilian, with a repertoire of sounds ranging from growls and croaks to snorts and snuffles. During the mating season or when wounded, it lets out thunderous roars.

# The Agile Snakes

All 2,700 kinds of snakes tend to look alike—long, squirmy and legless. But despite this superficial resemblance, they vary tremendously just as their ancestors the lizards do. They range in size from the five inches (12.7 cm) of a burrowing snake no thicker than a goose quill to the 30 feet (9.1 m) of an Asian python over 300 pounds (136 kg) in weight. And with these variations go others—environmental adaptations such as the prehensile tails of many of the arboreal snakes, or skin colors and patterns that match or blend with the surroundings. The amazing thing about snakes is that being legless has not proven a hindrance to locomotion, but an enhancement, making them extremely agile. Some snakes can even outdistance a man in brush or over rough ground.

THE EYELASH VIPER, a poisonous snake of Central America, can wind its prehensile tail several times around a branch and grab at birds with its open mouth while dangling in the air.

THE GREEN TREE SNAKE, colored to blend with Central America's foliage, reaches a length of four feet (1.2 m), but is so slender it can slither along branches without weighing them down.

THE BOA CONSTRICTOR, one of the most beautiful snakes, has a skin pattern harmonizing with shadowy jungle backgrounds. Dark stripes disrupt the head outline, and one disguises the eye.

THE KOMODO MONITORS of Indonesia, the largest, heaviest lizards, grow to 10 feet (3 m) and weigh up to 300 pounds (136 kg). They can catch small deer or pigs and tear them apart.

# The Dexterous Lizards

There are about 3,000 species and subspecies of lizards, and though they differ in many ways, they have one habit in common—all shed their skins. Adults molt once every month or so, during the months in which they are active, and unlike snakes, most do not shuffle off their epidermis in one piece, but in patches or even a scale at a time. The banded gecko below rips off its old skin with its mouth and swallows the strips. And to peel its feet, it yanks at each digit as though removing a tight glove.

THE BANDED GECKO OF THE SOUTHWESTERN U.S. BELONGS TO A FAMILY OF AGILE LIZARDS THAT IS MOST PREVALENT IN THE TROPICS. THIS LIZARD

MOLOCH HORRIDUS, named after an ancient god propitiated by child sacrifice, is covered with stubby spines and has two knobs over its eyes, which increase the size of its head. But despite its fearsome name, this Australian lizard is only eight inches (20.3 cm) long, moves slowly and deliberately, and lives on a diet of ants, lapping up from 1,000 to 1,500 at a meal.

COMES OUT ONTO THE DESERT FLOOR AT NIGHT TO HUNT INSECTS AND TWITCHES ITS TAIL IN CATLIKE FASHION JUST BEFORE LUNGING AT ITS PREY

A LEGLESS LIZARD from Florida so resembles an earthworm in both form and locomotion that it is often mistaken for one. Blind and without ear openings, it tunnels through damp soil, where it eats ants and termites. When exposed under a log, the foot-long (30-cm) worm lizard slides back into the burrow and uses the callused, blunt end of its tail to plug the hole after it.

A TINY SPUR, one of two located on each side of an anaconda's vent, is a vestigial leg. The male uses these movable spurs to scratch—and probably stimulate—the female during courtship.

## Snakes with "Legs," Lizards Without

Lizards are thought of as having legs and snakes as being legless, but this is not always strictly true. Such snakes as the anaconda, the boa constrictor and the python have vestigial hind legs that they no longer use for locomotion but can still move freely. The worm lizards, with the exception of three species, lack limbs, having lost them in the process of becoming burrowers. They live underground, mainly in the tropics, and tunnel through the earth with their heads. Their skulls are specialized for the task, with brain cases that are almost entirely enclosed and snouts that are often shovel-like, as in the Florida worm lizard at left. Other results of life underground include a soft skin folded into rings, shielded eyes reduced in size, a short tail and internal ears located along the sides of the jaw.

THE HEAD OF THE AJOLOTE, SMALL IN COMPARISON TO THE THICK BODY, HAS TINY EYES BENEATH THE SKIN AND IS WITHOUT EXTERNAL EARS

## An Odd Two-Legged Lizard

The ajolote, the two-legged worm lizard of Mexico's Baja California, is one of the Western Hemisphere's odd reptiles. Until recently, little more was known about it than that it lived underground in burrows and came out only at night. Oddest of all, it has two stout, clawed feet.

Just why the ajolote and two related Mexican species should have front legs, unlike other worm lizards, no one is yet able to say. Some authorities suspect that these three are the least specialized of

their family and therefore still in the evolutionary process of reducing and eventually losing their limbs. But the ajolote's legs are far from vestigial. The claws have a specialized bone structure, and the joints are reinforced to allow the legs to bend forward along the side of the body when preparing a new tunnel or widening a burrow. The ajolote uses its legs principally for burrowing and crawling over hard surfaces, with additional thrust supplied by serpentine or caterpillar movements of the trailing body.

MOLELIKE CLAWS of the ajolote are used for digging hard-packed soil, but when the earth is soft they are folded against the body and the blunt head does much of the work, twisting from side to side in an almost circular motion and bulldozing forward. The soft skin covering the legs and the underside of the body is so transparent that the blood vessels often show through.

# Lone Survivor of the Past

Sole living representative of the rhynchocephalians, a once widespread group of "beak-headed" reptiles, the tuatara has managed to hang on for 200 million years with only minor evolutionary changes in its skeleton. When it first came to the attention of scientists in 1831, it was identified as a lizard, which it superficially resembles, and a quarter of a century passed before a study of its anatomy revealed its uniqueness. Today, with its range limited to some 20 islands in New Zealand, the tuatara is the subject of extensive research and attempts are being made to find out why it did not disappear ages ago along with all its relatives.

The tuatara grows at a slow rate and probably does not reach sexual maturity until it is at least 20 years old. This would seem to make it one of the longest-lived of animals, and suggests that some of the full-grown males may be over 100 years old. Its eggs are believed to be fertilized nearly a year before being laid and take about 15 months to hatch —much longer than those of most other reptiles.

LAST HOME of the tuatara is two groups of very small New Zealand islands shown here by arrows and areas in solid color.

A BRIGHT-EYED TUATARA emerges from a hole under the roots of a small tree. Often the tuatara shares a petrel's burrow with the bird itself—and sometimes with the bird's eggs or young.

AN ALLOSAURUS skeleton is measured by two paleontologists at New York's Museum of Natural History. A meat-eating dinosaur of the Jurassic, it was 30 feet (9.1 m) long and weighed about two tons (1,814 kg).

2

# The Golden Age of Reptiles

No student of the history of life on earth will deny that the coming of the reptiles was one of the great events. As the first truly terrestrial vertebrates, the early reptiles not only filled out the faunal picture for their own time in arresting ways, but they also set the stage for later dramatic happenings like the rise of the dinosaurs, the beginnings of birds and the age-long evolution of the mammal line.

The reptiles waddled ashore about 325 million years ago, at the beginning of the Late Carboniferous. During the time of the coal forests, land vegetation had become well developed. Ferns, seed ferns and their kin covered the low-lying land, the energy of the sun was being caught and transformed by chlorophyll, insects had made their appearance and food was abundantly available on the shore. Yet it may not have been the hospitality of the land environment that led reptiles to occupy it so much as the inhospitality of the sea. Competition for a living in the water was increasing, partly because the sea environment was contracting as the oceans receded. Already some physical adaptations to life on land had evolved among the vertebrates that lived in shallow waters. They had acquired lungs and scales, and now they

## BY THEIR HIPS
## WE SHALL KNOW THEM

**TYPICAL SAURISCHIAN**

*Although the two dinosaurs shown here have a close external resemblance to each other, they actually represent two distinct groups: the saurischians and the orni- thischians. All dinosaurs belonged to one group or the other, and they are classified today by the kind of hipbones they had. The saurischian hips were quite like those of even more primitive reptile ancestors. The more specialized ornithischians de- veloped heavier, stronger hipbones which were particularly well adapted to a four- legged gait, although each group contained both bipedal and four-footed members.*

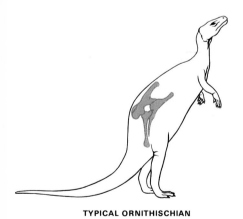

**TYPICAL ORNITHISCHIAN**

were developing functional legs and the shelled egg—characteristics essen- tial for life on the land.

The order in which these innovations appeared—as well as the immediate selective advantage each one bestowed—is still a subject of a good deal of controversy among experts. One fact is clear, however. Of all the adaptations that fitted the vertebrates into their increasingly refined roles on land, none was more fundamental than the reptilian egg.

Most people, thinking of an egg, think of a bird, but they are being led astray by seeing eggs mainly at breakfast. The birds did not invent the shelled egg, they inherited it, and it has undergone no important evolution in their possession. The first shelled land eggs were reptilian, and the reptiles were reptiles only when they had evolved such an egg. The old riddle, "which came first, the hen or the egg," is just whimsey when the hen is a bird. But applied to reptiles the question is valid, and paleontologists are still getting testy with each other trying to answer it.

THE reptiles came from amphibian ancestors. The egg of the usual amphib- ian is almost naked, enclosed only by a jelly envelope. The jelly supports each egg separately in the mass, keeps out small invaders and discourages predation by larger animals, but it gives almost no protection against drying up. A typical frog egg on land on a clear day will quickly wither. Thus, no matter how far the adult frog may be able to move from water in the course of its own daily activities, when it comes time to provide new frogs most species have to go home to the water. The songs of male frogs all over the world calling the females to the ponds show how strong the obligation is.

The egg as the reptiles developed it—which was essentially as we know it today—had no such limitation. The smooth shell tightly enclosed white and yolk, yet it was porous so as to allow necessary oxygen through. Like any egg, as it incubated it got more complex inside, but the complexity was not just in the forming body of the new animal. The structures required to keep the embryo alive in its shell—to keep it supported, fed, unpoisoned and unas- phyxiated—also had to evolve.

For the embryo to thrive, such an egg must be kept warm and not too dry, and must never be submerged for long in the water or it will suffocate. Thus the shelled egg, laid on land, is a kind of private sequestered pool in which a tender, beginning reptile can go through its perishable stages in much the same environment its ancestors lived in. The egg itself is a terrestrial adaptation, but the animal it harbors is still aquatic.

The shelled egg is thus the essence of the reptile. No amount of protection of any animal's adult stages will allow real pioneering on shore if the embryos remain unprotected. The adult can save its juices with scales, or it can move about to damp places to avoid drying up. But an embryo starts out as a helpless cell, almost without structure and without any capacity for movement at all, and it must be protected if it is to survive.

One of the frustrating facts about the fossil record of vertebrate history is that it shows so little about the evolution of reptiles during their earliest days, when the shelled egg was developing. There are three fundamental body features that the earliest land vertebrates had, and it would be very nice if we could draw a neat, clear, logical picture of the way in which these structures developed. These features are: legs, lungs, and a connection between nos- tril and pharynx that allowed the animals to breathe with their mouths shut.

Unfortunately for logic, these things were not started by the reptiles, nor even by the earlier amphibians. We must go even farther back, to the fishes, to find their beginnings. In trying to account for this, alternate explanations come to mind. Either the fishes that had the structures used them for some hidden purpose lost in time or their bearers actually did use them for what seems the obvious purpose of such an adaptation—going out on land. The latter is what paleontologists believe. The old lung-bearing, nose-breathing, stalk-finned fishes, known as Crossopterygii, remained fishes, but they apparently acquired the new adaptations in order to survive in the uncertainty of a shore-water environment that was subject to periods of drying up. Alfred S. Romer of Harvard pointed out that the first ventures ashore were probably not hunting trips, but most likely mud-slogging hegiras out of drying-up pools in search of better water. That is to say, the land-life equipment was at first used in search of ways to stay *in* the water rather than get out of it, at a time when the water was disappearing.

Over a great span of Paleozoic time we find adaptations to the terrestrial environment developing in four kinds of creatures, and it is logical to try to string them together into some kind of evolutionary sequence. First there were the stalk-finned fishes, then scaled amphibia known as labyrinthodonts, then some kinds of semiaquatic reptiles, and finally true land reptiles. These probably all belong to a single evolutionary line, but they overlapped in time, and the transition to a finished land reptile was certainly not a smoothly progressive adaptive process going hand in hand with a gradual movement farther into the land. On the contrary, like most things in the long, slow, millennia-consuming process of evolution, it had many fits and starts, blind alleys, repetitions and reversals. One theory even holds that the shelled egg evolved in a still-aquatic animal. A shell would have provided protection against the hazards of larval life in the water—and no doubt the teeming shore waters of Carboniferous seas and lagoons had predators aplenty to stimulate such a development.

THERE is another—and unusual—theory about how the reptiles got started and brought out the shelled egg. Coleman and Olive Goin suggested that the great advance occurred among creatures living in mountainous regions, where standing water was scarce, streams ran fast, and eggs laid in them were in danger of being swept away by the current. Aquatic eggs are usually fertilized outside the body of the female. A typical frog—presumably still following the pattern of the primitive amphibians—lays her eggs at the same time the male releases sperm into the surrounding water. Each egg is fertilized by the winner of a little race among the sperm. In fast water there might be no winners—the sperm might all be swept away, even if the eggs were not. Internal fertilization and a land egg go together nicely, because land eggs have shells that make external fertilization impossible since the sperm cannot get through the shell. So the Goins proposed that both the shelled egg and the behavioral pattern that allows it to be fertilized inside the body of the female before the shell is put on may have been an outcome of evolution of ancestral reptiles under pressure to develop ways to survive in rapid water in mountainous terrain.

This theory, of course, is as speculative as any of the others, but it follows the view prevailing today that both the primary anatomical adaptations and the shelled egg were acquired while the bearers were still in the water. And

## THE GEOLOGIC TIME SCALE

For many years experts have argued about the dates to be assigned to the eras, periods and epochs of the geologic time scale. The scale generally accepted for many years has been based on one devised by J. Laurence Kulp of Columbia University. More recently a scale compiled for the Elsevier Scientific Publishing Company has gained wide acceptance. The scale used in this book is an updated Kulp scale; its relationship to the Elsevier scale is shown in the table below.

| | DATE | |
| --- | --- | --- |
| | (MILLIONS OF YEARS AGO) | |
| | Kulp Scale | Elsevier Scale |
| **Paleozoic Era** | | |
| Cambrian Period | 600 | 570 |
| Ordovician Period | 500 | 500 |
| Silurian Period | 440 | 435 |
| Devonian Period | 400 | 395 |
| Carboniferous Period | | |
| Mississippian Epoch | 350 | 345 |
| Pennsylvanian Epoch | 325 | 310 |
| Permian Period | 270 | 280 |
| **Mesozoic Era** | | |
| Triassic Period | 225 | 230 |
| Jurassic Period | 180 | 195 |
| Cretaceous Period | 135 | 141 |
| **Cenozoic Era** | | |
| Tertiary Period | | |
| Paleocene Epoch | 70 | 65 |
| Eocene Epoch | 60 | 55 |
| Oligocene Epoch | 40 | 35 |
| Miocene Epoch | 25 | 22.5 |
| Pliocene Epoch | 10 | 5 |
| Quaternary Period | | |
| Pleistocene Epoch | 2 | 1.8 |

speculate we must, since neither behavior nor eggs fossilize well. But despite the trouble we have timing the separate steps toward the land, it is clear that before the Carboniferous was over, the "stem" reptiles, the cotylosaurs, had arisen. Their name derives from the fact that all later reptiles stem from them. During the Permian they diverged and set the stage for a number of important evolutionary events. They gave rise to the turtles, to the now-extinct ichthyosaurs (of which more will be said in the chapter on water reptiles), to the mammal-like reptiles, from which our own line has come, and to the thecodonts, the fated creatures that would give rise to the main figures of the Age of Reptiles. For it was these thecodonts that produced, among others, the "terrible lizards," the dinosaurs.

Subjectively speaking, as a sort of symbol of the inborn exuberance of protoplasm, no event of earth history can match the flowering of the dinosaurs. What man is doing is pretty fancy, but man is a single, separate sort of beast, not to be compared to the dinosaurs, which were a fantastically diverse group, all of them pure, authentic animals operating under the strong hand of natural selection. To put reptiles into a decent perspective I shall have to dwell for a little on the dinosaurs. Everybody should learn about them anyway. The study of dinosaurs is good for the human soul.

Dinosaurs first appeared in the Triassic, more than 200 million years ago. At the beginning they were not the giants one thinks of, but were mostly small, some no bigger than a chicken. Like a chicken, most were bipedal, walking or hopping about on their two hind legs. Though some showed four-legged adaptations, this two-leggedness was from the start an unmistakable and typical sign of the dinosaur line.

Some of the largest dinosaurs, such as *Brontosaurus*, the "thunder lizard," were four-legged. For this behemoth even four legs must have been barely sufficient to support a body weighing 80,000 pounds (36,288 kg), and some paleontologists conclude that *Brontosaurus* was primarily aquatic, depending on the buoyancy of water to relieve stress on its legs.

*Brontosaurus* is the best-known member of the Saurischia, one of the two great orders of dinosaurs that took shape toward the end of the Triassic. The second order, the Ornithischia, was made up exclusively of plant-eaters, while the saurischians included carnivores as well as herbivores. Both had four-legged and two-legged members, the main difference between the orders being in the structure of the pelvis.

THE saurischians included the biggest land vertebrates ever alive, such as the amphibious whip-tailed *Diplodocus* and the 50-ton (45.4-t) *Brachiosaurus*, the heaviest dinosaur of all. These had nostrils on the tops of their heads and could wade under water to search for soft vegetation. *Brachiosaurus'* nostrils actually protruded in a sort of hump that served as a snorkel. The most terrible carnivore, *Tyrannosaurus Rex* (king of tyrants), was also of this order. Standing almost 20 feet (6.1 m) high in its two-legged crouch, *Tyrannosaurus* was nearly 50 feet (15.2 m) long, including a four-foot (1.2-m) jaw with teeth like daggers.

While less fearsome, the ornithischian plant-eaters nonetheless included some of the most bizarre creatures the world has ever known. As the Cretaceous wore on they became more and more eccentric in their defensive paraphernalia, evolving horns, plates, cudgels and other forms of natural armor. The rhinoceros-like *Triceratops* had a thick protective skull that flared out like a shield over its powerful neck, two large horns projecting forward

## TWO MESOZOIC FLIERS

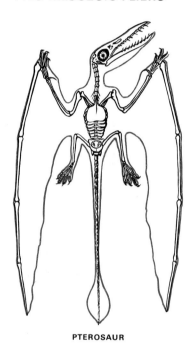

**PTEROSAUR**

*Although no reptiles can fly today, some did in the past. This long-tailed Rhamphorhynchus was one of these reptiles which took to the air some 180 million years ago. A big-jawed, toothy creature, it had an extremely elongated finger on each forelimb, providing a frame for its featherless wing. The other clawed fingers protruded for climbing. The tail ended in a rudder, aiding stability in flight. It had weak legs, probably walked little and cruised low over the water in search of its prey.*

from above its eyes and a third, shorter horn extending from its nose. The hulking *Stegosaurus* had vertical triangular plates along its spine from head to tail, possibly as defensive shields but also perhaps as heat-absorbing and heat-dissipating surfaces to help regulate body temperature. All dinosaur brains were tiny in comparison to body size, but *Stegosaurus* had, in effect, two. In addition to a walnut-sized brain in its head, *Stegosaurus* had in its hips a larger nerve center that controlled its hind legs and ponderous tail.

A CRETACEOUS event dwarfed by the towering phenomenon of the dinosaurs but critical to the future of reptiles was the advent of the snakes. The question of their ancestry is one of the most controversial problems in herpetology. They obviously came from lizards, but how? There are three principal hypotheses. The first is that the forebears of snakes were legless lizards to begin with, direct descendants of the fishes. This would explain the present leglessness of snakes. A second, related idea holds that snakes are not in a direct line with fishes but arose from one particular group of lizards, including some with legs (such as the ancient mosasaur and its surviving relatives, monitors and gila monsters) and the long-extinct *Tylosaurus*, 30 feet (9.1 m) long and legless, which fits the description of a giant sea serpent like the Loch Ness monster. Unfortunately, their link to snakes cannot be proved since all of them were giant aquatic animals or had good, functional legs. A third possibility is offered by the difference between the modern snake eye and the lizard eye. The snake eye appears to have degenerated during a long period as an organ of primitive burrowing lizards, then undergone a burst of secondary evolution into a useful organ of sight again when the snakes returned aboveground in more recent times.

All three explanations of snake origin remain speculation. It would help if a subterranean, blind, limbless monitor or mosasaur could be found, but so far none has turned up. Whatever the derivation of snakes may have been, and whatever the initial value of limblessness to the early snakes, there can be no doubt that an efficient new locomotor system has taken the place of the lost limbs. When they abandoned the four-point limb support for their bodies, the early snakes also removed limits to their lengths. They allowed serpentine movements to replace footwork and this laid the groundwork for other modifications as well. Constriction—killing of prey by squeezing it—is an example. Another is the series of tree-climbing adaptations of arboreal species, and the concurrent advantages of having a long body that can be made to look like a twig or branch. Also, losing the limbs and girdles and reducing the cross section of the body permitted snakes to go into places like narrow caves and crevices that would be closed to a four-legged animal of similar chest expansion. And for aquatic snakes the ability to swim by passing waves of undulation backward along the body made the loss of the limbs and lengthening of the body not merely acceptable, but advantageous.

To the modern snakes the lack of legs is not by any means a handicap to locomotion. Although for sheer speed over smooth ground most humans can move faster than most snakes, this is not true in cluttered places. Let the landscape be wooded, rough or scrubby and the snake a whip snake or racer, and a whole posse of people will be left behind in the chase.

Aerial locomotion—sustained flight—first achieved by the insects in the coal forests millions of years before, was evolved twice during the Age of Reptiles. The first venture was that of the pterosaurs, often called pterodactyls

**ARCHAEOPTERYX**

*The crow-sized Archaeopteryx, an ancient bird which lived toward the end of the era of flying reptiles, possessed many characteristics of the reptiles from which it sprang. Like the birds, Archaeopteryx was feathered and had strong hind limbs with claws adapted for perching. But it had a toothed, reptilian beak, claws on its forelimbs and a reptilian tail. Fossil remains indicate that the animal had a weak jaw and small teeth and, unlike the pterosaurs, probably fed on plants, insects and slugs.*

after one of their number, in the early Jurassic. These light-bodied creatures took to the air on leathery wings stretched by their finger bones. It is believed that some pterosaurs fed on the wing, dipping fish out of the sea like modern sea birds. The pterosaurs no doubt began as gliders, and some may never have become able to keep up sustained flapping flight. The biggest of them all, the Texas pterosaur discovered in 1971, would seem to have needed a mountain of muscle to flap its 50 feet (15.2 m) of wings. Yet its fossilized skeleton suggests that this huge scavenger actually did get off the ground under its own power, rippling its wings to take off from the lowlands and then gliding on warm air currents in search of dinosaur carcasses.

IN the Jurassic, some 150 million years ago, the reptiles made a completely different approach to the problem of flight. This other plan is revealed in some famous fossils found in Germany. The oldest representative of this other kind of aerialist is known as *Archaeopteryx*. Its skeletal structure is essentially that of a small, spry-looking dinosaur. But by vast good luck the faithful preservation of the body in the fine-grained Jurassic stone shows the clear imprint of a feather covering; in addition a relic in the British Museum has been identified as a fossilized *Archaeopteryx* feather. A feather means a bird. Feathers, obviously derived from the scales of reptiles, are the most distinctive feature of birds, and almost their only evolutionary innovation.

There are only a few obvious differences between birds and reptiles. To answer the demands of flight, birds have achieved a constant body temperature and a metabolic rate higher than that of reptiles. For lightness some of the bones have become hollow. A breastbone has developed for attachment of the flying muscles, and bones of the forelimb have been lost or bound together to support the wing along its leading edge. The teeth and the long reptilian tail are gone. Looked at with these differences in mind, *Archaeopteryx* is a wonderful example of an intermediate creature. Its jaws were toothed, its tail was long, its breastbone was weak and all its bones were solid. Its power of flight was surely feeble; but it had feathers, and it stands as a beautifully explicit link and sign of kinship between the nightingale and the crocodile. Archbishop Ussher himself, gazing upon *Archaeopteryx*, would embrace Darwinism, and would know at once where the birds came from.

The record of the derivation of mammals from reptiles is both far longer and far more detailed than the history of birds—and also, unfortunately, it is far less clear. It begins with the pelycosaurs of the late Carboniferous—a group not far removed from the old stem reptiles. Among these pelycosaurs may have been some that were warm-blooded rather than cold-blooded, and thus closer to their mammalian descendants than had been imagined. The peg-toothed *Dimetrodon*, for example, had a tremendous arching fin along its back, formed by a membrane stretched like a sail across vertical ribs. It is possible that, by regulating both the amount of blood flowing through this membrane and its direction to the sun, *Dimetrodon* could have kept its body temperature nearly constant. At least one of the dinosaurs, *Stegosaurus*, with its strange fins, may have shared this ability.

From the pelycosaurs there radiated a great array of types known as mammal-like reptiles, and during the late Paleozoic and early Mesozoic these creatures were the dominant vertebrates on the land. There is no missing link between mammals and reptiles, nor any single fossil type that, as *Archaeopteryx* does for birds, stands out clearly as half reptile, half mammal. If each

## ALIKE BUT UNRELATED

OSTRICH DINOSAUR

OSTRICH

*Many of the reptiles that appeared during the heyday of the dinosaurs were well adapted to ways of life that later were taken over by modern reptiles, mammals and birds. Since their habits were similar it is not surprising that their shapes were too. The eight-foot-tall (2.4-m) ostrich dinosaur, for example, was an omnivorous browser of plains. Like the modern ostrich, it had a toothless beak and strong legs.*

mammalian feature could be traced to its point of origin, we might hope to put a finger on the first mammals. As it is, the case rests mostly on bones and teeth, and relying on such skeletal characters alone, we only see the ancestral forms slowly acquiring the skeleton and dentition that today we associate with mammals. We can only deduce the scheduling of the less solid attributes not susceptible to preservation in the rocks.

Fortunately there are good clear differences in the skeletons of reptiles and mammals. One such is the structure of the jaw joint. Two bones enter this joint in both mammals and reptiles, but they are not the same kind of bones in the two animals. Furthermore, while in the mammal the lower jaw is a single bone, in the ancestral reptiles a number of bones are involved. Fossils from the late Triassic show various stages of reduction of jawbones, and a number of other characteristics that we now associate with mammals made their appearance at the same time.

By the Jurassic there were real mammals in the world. They were all small, insecure-looking creatures, and when we consider the kinds of beasts they shared the earth with we may justifiably wonder how they were able to hold on at all. There could be no better illustration of the vagaries of extinction and survival. After thundering about for 135 million years the dinosaurs have gone, and the hairy, feisty, rat-small creatures that cowered about their feet have inherited the earth.

The Age of Reptiles is an ideal time from which to draw graphic illustrations of the three great evolutionary processes: extinction, survival and adaptive radiation, the last being the tendency for a stock of living things to evolve in such a way as to exploit all the available opportunities of its environment. From its modest beginnings in the Triassic, the dinosaur line spread and split and sent out adaptive versions of itself into endless specialized roles and niches. The whole spectrum of Mesozoic life, furthermore, shows a similar trend. But because the adaptive radiation of dinosaurs was the most spectacular show put on by vertebrate animals prior to exploding the hydrogen bomb, the completely unexplained cutting off of all dinosaur lines in the Cretaceous is one of the most impressive cases of extinction that we know about. And when that extinction happens to a vast, noisy, exuberant and seemingly forever-entrenched crowd like the dinosaurs, it demands an explanation. But though a great deal of thought has been given to the matter, it still remains largely an impressive mystery.

MANY theories have been advanced to account for the immense dying of the dinosaurs. Some of them are almost persuasive, some seem pretty desperate. Any valid theory must take into account the fact that it was not a single species that disappeared so unaccountably, it was several *orders* of reptiles. It was a broad spectrum of animal life occupying many habitats. Some of the creatures were tiny, some gigantic, some ordinary reptiles, some among the most bizarre animals that ever lived. If too-great size, and thus too-great surface-to-volume ratio in time of rising temperatures killed off the sauropods, then what struck down the pterosaurs, most of which were wispy aerialists that lived in wholly different ways? If continental breakup and emerging mountains isolated the terrestrial dinosaurs, and mammals ate up their eggs, what plagued the live-bearing ichthyosaurs that ranged the open seas? And so it goes. One proposal blames the death of the dinosaurs on a supernova—a massive star that appears suddenly, shines very brightly and

**PHYTOSAUR**

**GAVIAL**

*There is an astonishingly close resemblance between the Triassic phytosaur, which became extinct 200 million years ago, and the gavial, a kind of crocodile found in Asia today. Both lived in swamps and on muddy riverbanks. Both were ferocious carnivores with long-toothed jaws for snatching fishes. But the phytosaur's nostrils were just in front of its eyes, while the gavial's are at the end of its snout.*

**PLACODUS**

**WALRUS**

*The eight-foot-long (2.4-m) Placodus was also a Triassic reptile. Its stout body, short neck and tail and paddle-like limbs resembled those of the modern walrus, a mammal. Like the walrus, it was a marine animal that dove to the bottom in search of shellfish which it crushed with its strong jaws and teeth. Although it lacked the canine tusks of the walrus, its front teeth were used as efficient nippers.*

then explodes, releasing huge amounts of radiation. In this case, the theory holds, the supernova was close enough to the earth to cause a sudden drastic temperature drop that the dinosaurs could not survive.

The dinosaurs were by no means the only Mesozoic reptiles that burgeoned and spread and then became extinct. Of the others, some made ventures into alleys that went quickly blind; others, like the ichthyosaurs and plesiosaurs, were successful radiations that endured far longer than modern mammals have been on earth. Many of them were stocks that went back into the sea, and more will be said of them in the chapter on water reptiles. The grand days of the crocodilians were the Mesozoic days, when one kind reached a length of 50 feet (15.2 m), and crocodile architecture was paralleled in astonishing detail by that of the phytosaurs, a completely separate branch from the Permian reptile stem. The crocodiles are still here; the phytosaurs, although in their own time they appeared to be just as promising, are gone, for reasons we do not know, and in all likelihood never will.

IT pays a creature like man to keep in mind the vast time spans of the "unsuccessful" lives of these cutoff bloodlines. In evolution, of course, there is nothing novel about lines becoming extinct. Extinction is the rule, and survival the breathtakingly improbable exception. When you look about at the animals and plants on earth today, what you see is the favored few. For every single stock running down into the present, thousands have been cut off. This applies not just to species, but to genera and families, and even to orders. During the Mesozoic, there were times when 16 orders of reptiles lived on earth at one time. Today there are four. One of these, the tuatara, is a single species with a drastically diminished range on a few New Zealand islands. Two of the orders are decadent, and only one, the Squamata, has shown recent evolutionary vigor. In brief, out of the whole teeming array of Mesozoic reptiles, only these stocks, listed here in the order of their branching out from the main reptile stem, remain on earth today.

(1) the mammals, which split off as the mammal-like reptiles about 300 million years ago;

(2) the turtles, which were probably derived during Permian times and were well developed by the Triassic;

(3) the crocodilians, which were derived from Triassic thecodonts;

(4) the tuatara, the only species of its order still alive, which has remained almost unchanged since its origin in Triassic eosuchian stock;

(5) the lizards and the snakes—the lizards having split off in the Upper Triassic, the snakes in the Cretaceous;

(6) the birds, which first appeared in the Jurassic in the intermediate form of *Archaeopteryx* and almost certainly were derived from Triassic thecodonts.

If we had been alive in the Age of Reptiles the great sight would have been the sweep of the deployment—the adaptive radiation of unprecedented types of life into unprecedented ways of living. Today, looking at what remains, we see the lesson of extinction and survival. The whole spirit of the grand, doomed days seems held in the small, cold body of the tuatara on the few chill islets of its dwindled range. Living on as unaccountably as the giants it once lived with died, it creeps out of its burrow in the evening, plods about in the mist to gather crickets to keep the old, small flame of its life alive; then, in the early morning, goes back again into the earth to which it has clung so stubbornly for some 200 million years.

THIS 42-FOOT-LONG (12.8-M) KRONOSAURUS SKELETON SHOWS THE MASSIVE BONES OF ONE OF THE LARGEST MARINE REPTILES EVER

# Days of Doomed Grandeur

Emerging from streams and ponds some 365 million years ago, the reptile ancestors established a beachhead during the Upper Devonian and eventually gave rise to myriad bizarre creatures, from gopher-sized cotylosaurs to the schooner-sized Brontosaurus. While many returned to the water, a few took to the air. But most remained on land to dominate the earth for some 200 million years.

# Evolution of Reptiles

LATE CARBONIFEROUS    PERMIAN    TRIASSIC

325 MILLION YEARS AGO

270 MILLION YEARS AGO

225 MILLION YEARS AGO

CYMBOSPONDYLUS

MESOSAURIA

MESOSAURUS

NOTHOSAURUS

PROTOROSAURUS

PROGANOCHELYS

COTYLOSAURIA
"Stem Reptiles"

HYLONOMUS

PROTOSUCHU

THECODONTIA

EUPARKERI

COELOPHYSIS

EOSUCHIA

YOUNGINA

OPHIACODON    EDAPHOSAURUS

CYNOGNATHUS

PELYCOSAURIA

DIMETRODON

MOSCHOPS    THERAPSIDA

DICYNODO

The reptiles' family tree is traced here from their Paleozoic origins as lizard-like Cotylosauria to their modern descendants. White areas show the major groups, when they arose, and how long they lasted. At least one member of each group is included. Broken lines indicate that fossil evidence for a particular link is sketchy or absent. The probable beginnings of birds and mammals are shown in brown to distinguish them as separate orders.

Many of the early reptiles would have been unrecognizable to us today. From the first cotylosaurs such as the Hylonomus they evolved over the millennia into frequently bizarre creatures of every shape and size, rulers of earth, sea and sky. The thecodonts *(left center)* of the Triassic gave rise not only to the flying pterosaurs and huge crocodiles that roamed the world, but also to elephantine ornithischians and saurischians, the dinosaurs. In their turn, saurischian dinosaurs were responsible for the evolution of the birds. Our own order, the mammals, came from four-legged reptiles of the therapsid group *(bottom)*.

The chart shows the relatively sudden extinction of the dinosaurs at the end of the Cretaceous. This "time of the great dying," when group after group of the most successful vertebrates in history simply vanished from the face of the earth, remains a mystery. Many paleontologists believe that the explanation may lie in a drastic climate change about 70 million years ago.

135 MILLION
YEARS AGO

70 MILLION
YEARS AGO

2 MILLION
YEARS AGO

URIA

*ICHTHYOSAURUS*

SAUROPTERYGIA

*PLESIOSAURUS*

*ELASMOSAURUS*

TURTLES
220 SPECIES

PROTOROSAURIA

CHELONIA

PTEROSAURIA

*MPHORHYNCHUS*

*PTERANODON*

CROCODILIA

CROCODILES
ALLIGATORS
21 SPECIES

*GEOSAURUS*

STEGOSAURUS

*CAMPTOSAURUS*

*PROTOCERATOPS*

ORNITHISCHIA

*SAURUS*

*TRACHODON*

*ANKYLOSAURUS*

*TRICERATOPS*

TO BIRDS

*ORNITHOLESTES*

*GORGOSAURUS*

*TYRANNOSAURUS*

SAURISCHIA

*BRONTOSAURUS*

TUATARA
1 SPECIES

RHYNCHOCEPHALIA

*HOMOEOSAURUS*

SNAKES
2,700 SPECIES

SQUAMATA

*MMALS*

*TYLOSAURUS*

LIZARDS
3,000 SPECIES

NYCTOSAURUS, a flying reptile, had elongated fourth-finger bones to support its seven-foot-wide (2.1-m) membranous wings, and was better adapted to soaring than flapping flight. Although most of its bones were hollow and birdlike, *Nyctosaurus* was neither a bird nor a bird ancestor. In fact, it was competition from the more efficient true birds that probably pushed *Nyctosaurus* and other flying reptiles to their long glide to extinction during the Cretaceous, some 70 million years ago.

## Infinite Evolutionary Variety from a Primitive "Stem" Ancestor

The world's great variety of vertebrate life got a major boost from the cotylosaurs, the first, or "stem," reptiles—the most important animals in reptilian history. These humble, ground-hugging creatures gave rise to a multitude of other reptiles, some of which in turn were the ancestors of birds and

DIADECTES, A "STEM" REPTILE AND ONE OF THE FIRST VERTEBRATE HERBIVORES, HAD FLAT GRINDING TEETH FOR MUNCHING FOREST PLANTS mammals. *Diadectes (below, left)*, with its thick body, short skull and sprawling limbs, was a member of this ancestral stock from which evolved such totally different creatures as *Nyctosaurus (above)*, a pigeon-sized flying reptile with an eagle's wingspread, and *Moschops (below, right)*, a ponderous plant eater.

**NYCTOSAURUS**
7 feet (2.1 m)

**DIADECTES**
6 feet (1.8 m)

**MOSCHOPS**
8 feet (2.4 m)

MOSCHOPS, WITH ITS THICK SKULL AND BODY, WAS ONE OF THE EARLY REPTILES TO RAISE ITSELF HIGH AND DEVELOP A MAMMAL-LIKE GAIT

UNEARTHED IN AUSTRALIA, THIS IS THE ONLY MOUNTED SPECIMEN OF KRONOSAURUS, A FRONT VIEW OF WHICH IS SHOWN ON PAGE 43.

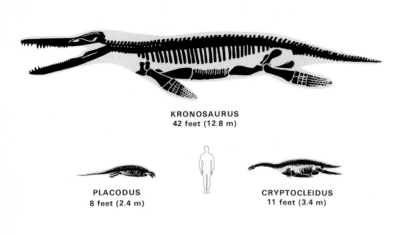

KRONOSAURUS
42 feet (12.8 m)

PLACODUS
8 feet (2.4 m)

CRYPTOCLEIDUS
11 feet (3.4 m)

PLACODUS, EIGHT FEET (2.4 M) LONG AND SMALL FOR A MARINE REPTIL

CRYPTOCLEIDUS, AN 11-FOOT-LONG (3.4-M), TOP-SWIMMING PREDATO

## Back to the Sea

After 70 million years of terrestrial living, some reptiles returned to the sea. One group, the sauropterygians shown on these pages, retained many reptilian characteristics, although their bodies became
more streamlined. All the sauropterygians developed hard rib "baskets" to support their abdomens
and protect their vulnerable undersides from attack.

Prominent among the sauropterygians was an important group called plesiosaurs. One of these was
*Kronosaurus (top)*, a fast-diving predator with huge,
fish-trapping jaws. Another was *Cryptocleidus (bottom)*, which used its long, flexible neck for pluck-
ing victims from passing schools of fish. *Placodus*,
in the middle, was not a plesiosaur; it was a lei-
surely bottom feeder that ground crustaceans to bits
with its mouthful of flat, crushing platelike teeth.

48

A NINE-FOOT (2.7-M) SKULL AND LARGE LIMB PADDLES. IT MAY HAVE EATEN ITS OWN KIND AS WELL AS SMALL MARINE CREATURES

PROBABLY A SLOW SWIMMER. BUT IT MAY HAVE FOUND PROTECTION FROM ARMOR ATTACHED TO NODULES ABOVE ITS VERTEBRAE

THE LATE JURASSIC, BELONGS TO THE LONG-NECKED SAUROPTERYGIANS, WHICH OFTEN HAD NECKS TWICE THE LENGTH OF THEIR BODIES

MYSTRIOSAURUS was a nine-foot (2.7-m) aquatic reptile of Europe. It belonged to a group of early crocodilians. Although *Mystriosaurus* lived some 150 million years ago, its fossils show quite an anatomical resemblance to crocodilians of today.

## Two Orders That Survived

Crocodilians and turtles have remained relatively unchanged for some 150 million years, having survived the mysterious disasters of the Mesozoic which wiped out most of the earth's reptile orders. The crocodilians seem to have parried extinction by adhering to a successful pattern of predatory existence. As long ago as the Jurassic, some primitive crocodilians already resembled, and presumably behaved much like, the later creatures to which they gave rise. One of these was *Mystriosaurus (above)*, which, like its modern counterparts, was armored with rows of bony plates, had a long, powerful jaw and prowled the shallows of tropical coasts.

When the prototypes of modern turtles appeared during the Triassic, they were largely terrestrial. These early creatures had already developed the characteristic turtle shell and had lost most of their teeth, their jaws being enclosed with horny beaks. Among the largest group, the Cryptodira, which appeared during the Cretaceous, there evolved types that could live almost anywhere, in deserts, swamps or open seas, and ate almost anything from leaves to lizards. Such flexibility contributed heavily to their survival. *Archelon (right)* was a seagoing cryptodire with characteristics of some of the modern marine turtles: a tough layer of skin in place of a shell, like the leatherbacks, and the inability to retract its neck completely.

ARCHELON, the largest turtle ever alive, was almost 11 feet (3.4 m) long and 12 feet (3.7 m) across at the flippers. The missing hind flipper may have been eaten by one of the fish or reptile predators that were *Archelon's* competitors in the Cretaceous seas.

SHELL AND ALL, a caiman lizard of
South America chews up a snail,
carefully spitting out the fragments
of the shell *(bottom)* before swallowing its contents. Its large flat teeth are
specifically adapted for this task.

3

# The Business
# of Eating

Most animals are at least to some degree shaped by the way they eat. Pursuers of live prey must be quick and agile, rooters and burrowers have special tools to help them find their food. So it is with reptiles. The wide range of their feeding habits is reflected in the great diversity of their appearance. Reptiles, like the other classes of land vertebrates, include both carnivorous and herbivorous members, and there are others that eat almost anything nourishing which the environment affords.

It was not always like that, however. The reptile ancestors were carnivores that were probably adapted originally to stalking and preying on live insects. Insects are small but relatively plentiful packages of highly concentrated energy, and along with such invertebrates as spiders and earthworms they are still the basic food for many reptiles. But there are numerous other reptiles that have altered their diets and feeding habits over millions of years. Their feeding adaptations fall into three basic categories: (1) equipment suitable for a herbivorous diet; (2) equipment making possible the swallowing of big—in some cases enormous—objects; and (3) equipment and behavior adapted to a special kind of food, like snails (opposite). Some insight into the evolutionary history of reptilian feeding habits can be obtained by taking a look at their individual development. In the embryonic and larval development of an animal there is often a tendency to repeat, in a crude sort of outline form, the stages of evolution by which the race was produced. This is never a rigid, detailed process of rehashing evolution, but simply a trend in which stages or structures repeat themselves in a broad and general way. Thus human embryos go through a stage when they have gill-like pouches which hark back to our remote fish ancestors. Similarly, most young reptiles, whatever diet they may choose in later life, begin as insect eaters.

It might, of course, be said that this is a practical necessity, since developing young need just such an abundance of neatly packaged, highly concentrated food as insects represent. But even granting that the eating of insects at this stage is only a case of opportunism, the sequence of events is nonetheless a repetition of the evolutionary events that preceded it. The first reptiles were insect eaters, and so today the young of reptiles return to the feeding habits of their ancestors. The offspring of the big tree iguana, which later in their lives will spend their days browsing and picking fruit off trees, begin by stalking and catching insects. The green sea turtle, almost totally herbivorous at maturity, starts by eating practically any animal food.

A SIMILAR progression from insect diet to some specialized sort of feeding is to be seen in various kinds of snakes, which as a group are the most elaborately specialized feeders among the reptiles. Here, however, the change is not from animal food to a diet of plants, but rather from an infantile habit of insect-eating to whatever restricted food the adults may specialize in. The rat snakes of the genus *Elaphe*, for instance, when grown show strong preference for warm-blooded prey and for eggs, but very young rat snakes eat nearly any living thing that they can catch and swallow. During their earliest weeks of life this means insects; later on frogs are added to the list, and when finally an adequate body size is reached, the adult diet of mice, birds and eggs becomes practicable. In all these cases the progression of feeding habits is clearly dictated by the relative availability of food that the animal is able to take in.

It is their leglessness that most obviously sets the snakes apart from the lizards, their fellows in the order Squamata. Actually, however, feeding adaptations were also behind the initial evolutionary separation—and these are fully as striking as their lack of legs. The whole structure of a snake's head and jaws, for instance, is designed to provide the stretch that allows it to take in creatures bigger around than itself. This ability obviously gives snakes greater scope in their feeding outlook and, indeed, most adult snakes will either eat anything live that they can swallow or show some kind of curiously specialized food preference, like *Dasypeltis*, an African genus which eats only eggs. It might even be said that the gape of the snake made the snake plan feasible. In any case, of all the many ventures into limblessness which the Squamata have made, the only one that prospered markedly was the one that accompanied this extraordinary ability to accommodate oversized food.

Most lizards, on the other hand, have continued in the traditional insect-eating role. Though some among them will occasionally pick up small pieces of bread or bits of fruit thrown to them, eating pieces of objects rather than whole objects is really out of character for the Squamata.

In eating very small prey, lizards simply grab and swallow, but when they feed on larger animals they use a swallowing technique called inertial feeding.

Objects too big to be taken in forthwith are seized and then engulfed by a process involving a sudden relaxing of the jawhold, followed by a quick sideways thrust that moves the jaw a little farther over the object. The grip is again relaxed, the axis of the head is shifted the other way, and a new bite is made with the other side of the jaw forward. The inertia of the object gives the advancing jaws something to push against. That lizards carry out the process by moving first one side of the jaw forward and then the other forecasts the far more specialized "jaw-walking" method of swallowing carried out by snakes.

The feeding technique of snakes is, as noted, one of their fundamentally distinctive features, and it involves some remarkable structural modifications of the head and jaws. Besides reductions in the facial skeleton which free the jaws from the brain case behind, the brain itself is encased in bone as a protection against contact with the oversized and often resisting food. The front ends of the lower jaw are not tightly joined at the chin, but only loosely connected by a ligament. Each of the lower jawbones is thus a freely movable unit. This gives the mouth a monstrous gape and stretch limited only by the elasticity of the soft tissues of the mouth and throat. To this arrangement are added recurved teeth and a complex set of muscles that operate in a way that allows each side of the jaw to be manipulated separately. The snake takes in its food by simply moving one side of the jaw forward to a toothhold, then walking the other side alternately a little farther still, then going back to the first side and moving it up again, and so on. The recurved teeth hold the prey firmly while the jaw is biting but disengage freely as each side is alternately pushed forward for a new grip.

It is not surprising that snakes have evolved a number of supplementary adaptations to help exploit their gape. To avoid interruption of its breathing, for example, a snake swallowing a big rat or frog extends its glottis beyond the end of the lower jaw and through it takes in air as a diver breathes through a snorkel tube. Another modification related to feeding is constriction, a maneuver by which the snake throws turns of its body around the prey and suffocates it by squeezing it. The coils of a constrictor are thrown on with incredible speed, and control in some cases is so good that a rat snake, for instance, can entwine and kill at least three baby rabbits at the same time, thus making the most of the opportunity offered by a rabbit nest.

To most people constricting seems one of the more lurid and unpardonable things that snakes do, and through the centuries the habit has evoked a great deal of morbid lore. For example, though I come from an enlightened family, I grew up thinking that a constricting snake snatches up its prey, throws on coils and with chiropractic precision pulverizes each separate bone in its victim's body, licks the pulped prey all over to lubricate it, zestfully engulfs it and then lays up somewhere for a year or more, stupefied by its excesses.

Only part of this is true. The speed with which the coils are applied is striking and the force they exert is great. There is rarely any crushing of bones, however, no laving with slime till the food is on the way down and in most cases little shaping and molding of the victim's contours for easy swallowing.

Although pythons and boas usually come to mind first when we think of constrictors, the constricting habit is more widespread among smaller snakes. Perhaps the most diminutive is the slender short-tailed snake of central Florida which overpowers other little snakes for eating by squeezing them into quiescence—just as its bigger relative the king snake also does. The same musculature that is used in constricting is also useful in climbing trees and most, though

## HOW SNAKES SWALLOW LARGE OBJECTS

**Quadrate bone**

**SNAKE JAW CLOSED**

*A versatile jaw enables snakes to swallow their food headfirst and whole, even when the victim is larger in diameter than the snake's body, and may even be alive and kicking. The quadrate bone, connecting the lower jaw loosely to the skull, works like a double-jointed hinge so that the snake can drop its lower jaw at the back of its mouth as well as at the front. The lower jaw can also be stretched sideways, since its two halves are connected at the chin by an elastic muscle. Sharp, recurved teeth hold the quarry in place while the snake, moving first one side and then the other of its mobile jaws, seems to "walk" its gaping mouth forward around its food.*

**SNAKE JAW DISTENDED**

not all of the constricting snakes are partly arboreal. Just as remarkable as constriction, and even more refined as a device used by snakes for taking big prey, is venom injection. Some of the consequences of this extraordinary feeding device will be discussed further on.

As a group, then, the snakes can be regarded as the most strongly modified reptiles in regard to food-taking adjustments. Theirs is a broad-scale specialization, however, involving the whole suborder to which they belong. Throughout the class Reptilia, curious side ventures in hunting or food-taking may be found in single genera or even species.

Turtles are on the whole the least elaborate feeders among reptiles, but they too have their specialized members. The classic examples are two unlovely creatures that live on the bottoms of streams and sloughs and take prey by ambush. One is the aforementioned South American matamata; the other is the alligator snapper of the southeastern United States, which not only uses camouflage as the matamata does, but adds to this a fishing lure for decoying victims.

THE alligator snapper is a big, dun-colored turtle with a three-keeled shell, a huge lumpy head, strong jaws, and musculature that snaps the jaws forward and shut in a lightning-fast strike. Other turtles are able to strike as fast and powerfully, but the alligator snapper has something extra to draw prey within reach. In murky water it looks like a lump of mud or part of the bottom. Its shell and swollen head are generally scarred, eroded, and bearded with algae. Even its eyes are camouflaged by a broad turret of skin that protrudes from the margins of the orbit and partly surrounds the eye, which thus peers out from the depths of a little hole. The device is strikingly like that of the turreted eye of an African chameleon and evidently serves the same general function. The small area of iris visible is spread with black spots, each comparable to the pupil in size, and by the redundance of these the pupil itself is rendered meaningless to the observer. At least, that is the way it looks to a human observer and the alligator snapper certainly seems to use this equipment as useful camouflage in feeding. It spends a great deal of its time lying in the murk with its jaws wide open, sometimes still, sometimes with its head swaying slowly back and forth. Look inside its mouth, and if the light is good enough you will see what appears to be the two ends of an earthworm fastened in the middle by a short stalk from the floor of the mouth. The object looks like a worm, and it is quite clearly used as a lure to attract fishes into striking distance. It is under complete muscular control, and can be pointed in any direction and extended and contracted in ways strikingly similar to the contortions of an earthworm that finds itself in water. I have never seen a fish grab this bait, but others have. And many times I have seen an alligator turtle open its jaws wide the instant a fish came near, then move the "worm" about suggestively in a way that ought to appeal deeply to any fish not aware that this was actually part of a fish-eating turtle.

The matamata is the most thoroughly inanimate-looking of all turtles—perhaps of all vertebrate animals. Its weird appearance is not simply a misfortune,

## MECHANICS OF THE CHAMELEON'S TONGUE

*For years it was thought that the tongue of the chameleon, which is hollow, was "blown" out of its mouth like the finger of a glove. Now it is understood that its firing is under the control of two sets of muscles. One set runs the length of the tongue and keeps it packed in tight pleats on a pointed bone in the back of the mouth like a spring coiled on a stick.*

*When the chameleon spots an insect it opens its mouth, moves the whole apparatus forward, and contracts a second set of muscles that circle the tongue like a series of tiny automobile tires. When contracted, they tend to squeeze the tongue forward off the central bone (top). The chameleon "fires" by suddenly relaxing the long muscles; the tongue shoots forward like a released spring (bottom), given more impetus by a squeezing action of ring muscles.*

but rather a clearly utilitarian adjustment to a way of getting food. The matamata not only looks like a pile of debris, but its limbs and grotesquely flattened head are fringed and festooned with shreds and filaments of itself that should, and must, seem to a small fish like edible refuse. In any case, small fishes do come up and nibble and snatch at these projections, and are often quickly sucked in by a remarkable sort of hydraulic trap the matamata uses in place of the strike and jawhold of the snappers and soft-shelled turtles. The matamata's jawbones are weak and rubbery, serving as little more than a hooplike support for the front edge of the greatly distensible mouth and throat. As the head shoots forward at the prey the jaws open wide, the throat distends tremendously, sucking a quick flood of water into the mouth, and washing in anything in the neighborhood that is not strongly anchored.

Except for these and a few other cases of specialization for ambush, turtles are mostly straightforward, simple feeders and some of them, like the American box turtles, are the most nearly omnivorous of any reptiles.

Odd or narrowly specialized diets are more commonly found among snakes and lizards. There are, for instance, lizards that specialize in ants. The Asiatic gliding lizards of the genus *Draco* are among these and since *Draco* is arboreal, it finds its chief source of food among tree-dwelling species of ants. The horned lizards of the American West, and the marvelously spiny Australian moloch are other anteaters. It was pointed out earlier that no one knows why such a habit should be furthered by having the wild and spiky appearance that horned lizards and molochs have.

The African egg-eating snakes of the genus *Dasypeltis* have become specifically modified for a diet of eggs. Various other kinds of snakes eat eggs, of course, but *Dasypeltis* is commited entirely to the exploitation of the habit. The eggs have to be eaten whole—a snake's tongue is too wispy to lap up their contents. For a handless creature to engulf a big, smooth, oval egg with a surface too hard for a toothhold seems next to impossible—a feat compared to which bobbing for apples is the merest child's play—and the accomplishments of *Dasypeltis* in this line are imposing. The distensibility of its mouth is perhaps greater than that of any other snake. The lining of the mouth, when not stretched around an egg, lies in folds and pleats. While most kinds of snakes, when they have swallowed an egg, either break it by contractions of the body wall or simply wait for the shell to dissolve, *Dasypeltis* has sharp projections from the neck vertebrae that rip the shell open as it goes down the gullet. There is a special set of muscles for regurgitating the shells, and a valve for keeping the liquid egg-contents down while the shells come up. What advantage *Dasypeltis* finds in specializing so narrowly is not clear. Perhaps it is just that being exclusively an eater of eggs allows one to be a very successful eater of eggs.

There is a whole subfamily of slender tree snakes, the Dipsadinae, that feeds mainly on slugs and snails. Both their tooth equipment and their psychology are specialized for overcoming the reluctance of a sticky snail to come out of a shell which would be a nuisance to swallow. There are turtles and lizards that eat snails too, but most of them crudely smash up the shells with flat jaw surfaces or blunt teeth, swallow fragments of them along with the occupant and are then faced with the job of defecating the broken pieces. As if to show the greater refinement of snakes in all dietary matters, *Dipsas* has developed a specially modified lower jaw, and plucks out the snail with elongated teeth. The most parochial of all reptile victualers I have heard of is a little burrowing snake, without a common name, known technically as *Leptotyphlops phenops*. It feeds on the contents of termites' abdomens which it apparently sucks out of the skin, leaving it and the thorax behind. Besides being strangely restricted, this diet is also the only one among snakes that involves the taking of pieces of a food object rather than the whole thing. All the rest of the snakes eat whole objects, with none of the chewing or tearing apart of food practiced by cro-codilians and by some turtles.

One of the most refined hunting devices among reptiles is the insect-trapping tongue of the true chameleons. The tongue can be popped out for a distance equal to about one and a half times the length of the body of the animal, not including the tail. The end of the tongue is an enlarged bulb covered with an adhesive that will hold good-sized active prey—mostly insects, but sometimes even small birds and reptiles. A toad, of course, also uses a sticky tongue as an insect trap, but the way the chameleon shoots its tongue forward is very dif-ferent. The tongue of the chameleon is hollow, and when not in use is bunched up, accordion-like, on a smooth, tapered cartilaginous projection of the bony throat structure, or hyoid apparatus. As the chameleon approaches a victim— which it does with diabolical stealth—the whole tongue assembly shifts to a ready station toward the front of the mouth. The force that shoots the tongue out when it is triggered is a spasmic contraction of a ring of muscle built into the structure of the forward section of the tongue. This squeezes down on the lubricated taper of the spike of cartilage like two fingers squeezing down on a watermelon seed, except that in this case it is the squeezing tongue that shoots out. At the same instant opposing muscles let go, and the tongue runs forward so fast that it flies out full length before it is finally stopped by elastic fibers in its wall. It is withdrawn by contractions of longitudinal muscles.

The chameleon is as fully committed to living in trees as any reptile in the world and its tongue is a trap for small tree-dwelling creatures. The tongue trap would not work very well on the ground. There are generally too many obstructions close to the ground for such long-range shooting; moreover, the tongue sags at the end of the trajectory and its sticky surface would pick up dirt. In any case, chameleons are arboreal and their whole architecture is adjusted to living in trees. Their twig-grasping feet look like the jaws of pliers. Their eyes roll about freely, wholly independent of one another, hidden in the depths of ported turrets that shield their glint except from the ill-fated crea-ture on which they focus, and for whom the glint would generally come too late.

THE famous chameleon color-changes range through a variety of hues and shifts of pattern. Most chameleons are able to assume colors and patterns that blend into their surroundings. The dwarf chameleons of the genus *Brooke-sia* have more or less fixed patterns and a body form that in silhouette suggests a leaf. In southern Malawi I once came upon three of these fat little lizards in deep rain forest on the southern slopes of Mount Mlanje, all unaccountably on the ground and all plodding the same way across the dim trail I was following. I have no idea what they were doing down there out of the trees, but they seemed to have in mind some place to go; and seeing three of them within a hundred yards (91 m), tottering ahead on pincer feet, was like witnessing a ritual migra-tion of some mysterious kind. Though the migratory band was only three, it was quite an event for me because the Mlanje dwarf chameleon is a scarce animal.

Adaptations are neither acquired nor used in a vacuum. From the start, and increasingly as they are perfected, new structures and functions are bound to affect and be affected by the whole organization of the animal. A modification occurs, and there follows a whole system of other changes to compensate for it or to exploit it. The idea is beautifully shown in some of the ramifications of venom production in reptiles, which is clearly related to the basic snake specialty of going after oversized food too active to be merely seized and swallowed.

Of all the feeding adaptations of reptiles, the ability of certain snakes and of the lizards, the Gila monster and its close relative the Mexican beaded lizard, to kill prey by the injection of poison seems the most dramatic. The poison of snakes fascinated men long before Cleopatra clutched the famous asp to her bosom, and it has probably inspired as much myth and folklore as any adaptation in the animal kingdom. Humans, of course, experience it primarily as a defensive weapon used by the snakes, since man is not a part of any poisonous reptile's food plan; but man has a way of making these things his own, forgetting the main and original purpose which such adaptations serve—in this case, the procuring of food. Thus the lore and legend of snake venom usually revolves around human experience, and the rabbit or rat or other small mammal that is the normal victim of a poison snake dies and is eaten in obscurity.

Reptile poison is modified saliva. All snakes have well-developed salivary glands, the secretions of which help to lubricate the big objects that their wide gape allows them to swallow. In the venomous snakes, certain of these salivary glands have been converted into poison producers. In the poisonous colubrids, for instance, a gland just under the lip scales sends venom into grooved, fixed teeth in the rear of the upper jaw. In the vipers it is another gland, located below and behind the eye, that produces the poison and pipes it forward through a slender duct to the base of the fang.

Snake venom is made up of a variety of active substances, mostly proteins and enzymes. Some of these act principally on the circulatory system, clotting blood cells and destroying capillary walls. Such poisons are called hemotoxic or hemorrhagic. Other snake venoms are neurotoxic, acting mainly on the nervous system, paralyzing muscles of the heart or breathing apparatus or both. Although there is a great deal of individual and specific variation in the make-up and strength of venoms, the vipers in general have poisons of the former type, killing by circulatory disruptions, heavy bleeding, and destruction of tissues, while the venom of cobra-like snakes in general paralyzes the prey.

The needles for the hypodermic injection or introduction of venom are, of course, modified teeth. In Gila monsters they are several grooved teeth in both the upper and lower jaws. Poison seeps into the grooves from furrows in the lining of the mouth which lead from multiple gland-openings, a rather inefficient arrangement that makes it impossible for these lizards to use the swift stab of the poisonous snakes—instead they must bite and hang on. Fangs of the cobra group retain traces of a groove on the fore margins, showing that they formed by infolding along the anterior surface. Some cobras are able to spit their poison. The herpetologist Charles Bogert made a careful study of cobra fangs and found that their unsettling ability to throw a fine stream of poison several feet ahead can be explained by the arrangement of the opening at the fang tip. This is so placed that venom under pressure from behind comes out at right angles to the long axis of the tooth. Among most poisonous snakes the venom holes are at the tips of fangs. For such a snake to squirt venom forward and upward at a useful angle to hit something in front of it, it would have to have an unreasonably wide gape even for a snake, and in addition would have

## HOW A RATTLESNAKE RELEASES VENOM

**VENOM APPARATUS**

*When a rattlesnake opens its mouth to strike, its long fangs, which have lain folded flat along the roof of its mouth, are swung into the position shown in the drawing above, and can be plunged into the victim's flesh with one swift jab of the snake's head. As the fangs sink in, muscles contract and squeeze a venom gland in each cheek, forcing the poison out through a narrow tube that runs from gland to fang.*

**FANG OF RATTLER**

*A cross section of a rattler's fang reveals the hollow tube that carries venom (shown in color) from the venom sac to a hole near the tooth's tip. This is the most efficient way for snakes to conduct poison. In others the poison trickles along an open canal or even a simple groove in the fang and may spill out. But by conserving its venom in a closed pipeline, the rattlesnake can fell its victim with a single bite.*

## WARNING DEVICES

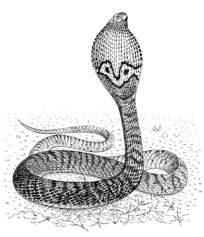

**THE INDIAN COBRA**

*Confronted by danger, the cobra flattens the skin of its neck into a wide hood, which makes it look bigger than it is. It does this by spreading long, movable ribs.*

**THE RATTLESNAKE**

*To warn away enemies, the rattlesnake shakes the hollow segments that form the rattle at the end of its tail. Each time it sheds its skin, it adds one new section.*

**THE CORAL SNAKE**

*The red, yellow and black bands of the venomous coral snake act as a warning flag to other animals. Some harmless species imitate its stripes to bluff their enemies.*

to tilt its head far back over its body. In the case of a spitting cobra, because the hole at the fang tip faces forward, it is able to discharge its poison with the mouth only slightly agape. There is some question as to the utility of the spitting adaptation. Although it blinds victims temporarily, or even permanently, it cannot be thought of as an effective way of immobilizing prey, and thus must be an adaptation for discouraging potential enemies.

In vipers the fang canal is completely and smoothly enclosed. Viper fangs are very long, and to keep them from piercing the floor of the mouth they fold back against its roof by a rolling movement of the shortened maxillary bone on which they are mounted. One or more pairs of spare fangs are usually arranged in formation behind the pair being used. Because the duct from the poison gland fits over the base of the spare teeth as well as over that of the fang in use, the loss of a fang does not hold up matters at all—the spare comes forward, alongside the functional fang, and is ready for use.

To show how the consequences of an adaptation like poison are spread through the whole makeup of an animal, it is interesting to examine the rattlesnake. Like most snakes, rattlesnakes take live prey, and their poison enables them to take relatively large animals with a minimum of effort and risk. Being snakes, they also show the drastic remodeling of the head that lets them swallow big food—which has the dual advantage of increasing the number of different kinds of things they can eat and enabling them to go longer on one meal, if that meal is a big one.

All of this depends, of course, on the rattler's being able to find, immobilize and, without being injured in the process, swallow the prey and then digest it properly—and all of its equipment is geared to do just that. To detect the nearness of warm-blooded prey, even in the dark, rattlesnakes (and all of the pit vipers) have the heat-feeling pits characteristic of their kind. These are cavities a little larger than the nostril, located on either side of the snout between the nostril and the eye. They are sculptured out of the maxillary bone and are lined with sensory cells specially designed to detect changes in radiant heat. They evidently are the counterparts of less elaborate pits in the lip scales of boas and pythons which have been shown to function in a similar way. These tell the rattlesnake of the presence of warm-blooded animals as far as a foot and a half (46 cm) away, and help guide the range and direction of the strike.

Once the victim has been stabbed, the poison immediately comes into play, and since it contains a spreading agent to speed its distribution, its effects are sure. The victim rarely drops dead in its tracks (although I once saw a fox terrier fall three yards [2.7 m] from where it had been bitten by a six-and-a-half-foot [2-m] diamondback rattler), but usually runs off in a panic and falls some distance away. For this reason the rattlesnake's specialized feeding equipment should be designed to cope with this situation too—and it is, in the form of the adaptation known as Jacobson's organ.

This organ comprises a pair of cavities located internally on each side of the snout with ducts leading to an opening in the roof of the mouth. The cavities are heavily supplied with nerve endings like those used in the smell sense. The tongue picks up odorous particles from the ground or out of the air itself and transfers them to the openings of Jacobson's organ, thus enabling the rattlesnake to trail its victim. Although the process seems to overlap the regular olfactory sense, it does not replace it. Many reptiles with well-developed Jacobson's organs are able to smell in the ordinary way too. This curious organ is not used in food-getting alone, but seems to be put to important social uses such as the forming of hibernating groups and the finding of one sex by another at mating time. Nevertheless, its part in the complex of feeding adaptations of the rattlesnake is evident. It is the only link that the poisonous snake has with the poisoned, doomed but still mobile prey.

Once the rattlesnake has caught up with its now dead or dying victim, it brings to bear the snake-wide ability to fit its jaws over huge packages of food. A four-foot (1.2-m) rattler can swallow a grown cottontail rabbit. Moreover, it is able to provide itself with cottontails to swallow, something a nonvenomous snake could only rarely do. Nor does the interaction of adaptations end there. Because snake venom contains digestive enzymes, the process of digestion begins as soon as the venom diffuses into the tissues of the prey. This, too, is important in terms of economy of effort. Nonpoisonous snakes, especially the constrictors, which subdue big prey by squeezing them into immobility, must digest without the help of any internal enzyme action in their food. But for the rattlesnake, digestion of the huge bulk proceeds from the inside as well as at the surface, and there is little doubt that the time involved is greatly shortened —with whatever attendant profit the saving of time might yield to the snake.

The usefulness of venom is not confined to feeding alone. Its potential advantages as a defense mechanism are obviously also powerful. However, this point is not so simple as it might seem at first glance. For while it is clear that poison is a good thing to stay away from, how will another animal know that a snake is poisonous? The question leads to some interesting conclusions.

In feeding activity, of course, there is no conceivable reason why a snake should warn its prey of its venomous intentions. To convert feeding mechanisms to defense, however, either against attack by snake-eating predators or against the hazard of being accidentally trod upon by heavy animals of any sort, some means of advertisement—a warning system—that will prevent the attack would seem to be required. Violent encounters in nature are generally disadvantageous, even to a poisonous snake, and any device that will reduce their frequency is bound to be a good thing to have. It is evidently for this very reason that coral snakes are usually brilliantly colored and marked, that cobras rise high and spread spectacular hoods, and that the rattlesnake sounds its rattle.

IT may never be possible to prove satisfactorily that a rattlesnake evolved its rattle as a safety device, but common sense certainly supports this conclusion. Such mechanisms, however, if they actually work as they seem to, work in a complicated way. They must depend for their effect on a reactive mechanism in the potential enemy—that is to say, a concurrent evolutionary change that might produce in deer, for example, a tendency to shun fancily banded snakes or in coyotes to jump away from the buzz of a rattlesnake's rattle. This is not hard to imagine, however. There are abundant cases in nature in which two different kinds of animals go through concomitant evolutionary changes that fit them for beneficial contacts with each other or reduce friction between them. In the relationships among living things harmony is at least as important as strife as a means of survival. A crab may cause havoc among the small animals that are its food, but at the same time it tolerantly goes about with a sea anemone on its back, or even makes overt moves to put the anemone there. The stinging cells of the anemone are protection for the crab, and the scraps from the crab's feeding are eaten by its partner. Though at first glance it may seem silly to use such an example to illustrate the relationship between poisonous snakes and other animals, it is not silly at all. Both the rattlesnake and a bison, say, are potentially dangerous to each other. Neither can get the slightest good out of contact with the other. On the other hand, both can profit immensely by staying cleanly out of one another's way.

What, then, is more logical than that the snake should evolve a warning device, and the potential enemy—the inadvertent trampler—the psychology to react to the warning? Even a carnivore that usually ate snakes—unless it was immune to snake venom—would logically be better off if it had a heritable ability to recognize, or to *learn* to recognize, harmful snakes. Then it could go about its business of eating harmless snakes without any trouble. The candy-stick coloration of coral snakes would surely entrench any such discriminatory capacity as might be found naturally in a coon or a hawk or any other snake-eating predator. So would the rattlesnake's hair-raising song.

T HE idea of a poisonous animal evolving a warning device that will work only if a potential enemy also evolves the sense to react to the warning is hard for some people to accept. I do not know why this should be so. Besides logic, a great store of anecdotal evidence supports its reality. Nearly any mature Florida bird dog, for instance, reacts instantly to the sound of a rattlesnake. While it is hard to be sure what a dog has learned from previous experience or from other dogs, it can in most of the cases I know about be confidently said that the learning process did not involve being bitten by a rattlesnake. A pointer I used to hunt with in central Florida, though it had never been bitten by a poisonous snake in its life, showed unmistakable evidence of associating the rattle with a particularly odious situation. In its quartering for quail, if you saw it suddenly jump into the air and you went to the spot to see what had scared it, one of two things was most often there—a coiled diamondback, or a bush of a certain species of *Crotalaria*, the dry pods of which rattle when disturbed, almost like a rattler's alarm. Only one of the several species of *Crotalaria* sounds authentically like a snake, and only that species used to make my dog jump. But the effect of a collision with that was electric, and for all the years of its life the dog rose like a bird when it stirred the fearful noise from a diamondback or from the bush that I think sounded the same to the dog.

That is of course not a scientific observation. It involves a subjective judgment on my part, and the behavior of only one dog. And it in any case leaves unanswered the question whether the reaction is innate in canines or is learned by associating the sound of the rattle with the bites or aggressive behavior of snakes in general—or is learned from other dogs. That dogs are of Old World —and rattlesnakes of American—origin makes it unlikely that the pointer was born genetically able to associate the sound with the snake. On the other hand, the buzzing of rattlesnakes is really just an elaboration of a tendency of many kinds of snakes to vibrate the tail when approached by a potential enemy. The vibration is often soundless, but in dry leaves it makes a little rattling or humming noise. Possibly dog ancestors evolved the capacity to associate such a sound with ill-tempered or dangerous snakes. But the important point is that the rattle of the rattlesnakes makes little sense unless it can be thought of as an agent of advantage to the bearer. And the advantage in not being stepped on by a bison or chopped up by the teeth of a wolf seems pretty clear. That the bison and wolf might go away poisoned and die after trampling or chewing up the reptile would be little comfort to the snake. Its profit would come from preventing the encounter from happening.

A CALIFORNIA KING SNAKE LUNGES AT A WARY KANGAROO RAT. ITS DIET CONSISTS OF MANY RODENTS AND SNAKES, INCLUDING RATTLERS

# The Snake as Hunter

Of all reptiles, snakes are the most highly specialized hunters and feeders. Be they small as worms or bigger than the king snake above, they all subdue and swallow live prey, eating meat exclusively with an economy of risk and effort which few animals of any kind can match. The portfolio of photographs on the following pages records their vigor as trenchermen, their skill as hunters.

63

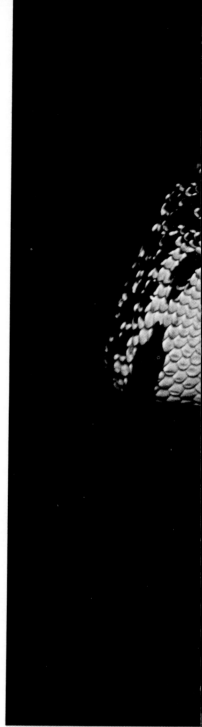

SQUEEZING STEADILY, a pine snake kills a white rat. Constrictors do not crush their victims, as many people have long thought; their coils make it harder and harder for the prey to breathe until it finally suffocates.

WITH A GOOD GRIP on the head of an anole lizard, this vine snake will settle itself and slowly swallow it. Vine snakes are long and slender; they lurk in foliage and pounce on lizards creeping among the leaves.

## The Devices of Snakes for Subduing Food

Though limbless, lethargic and small-brained, the snake is one of the most perfectly efficient predators in the animal world. Elastic jaw joints let it accommodate any prey of reasonable size. A slim body lets it prowl or lie in ambush inconspicuously. A slow metabolism enables it to wait weeks for the right meal. If food walks by that might put up a dangerous fight, a snake can usually afford to ignore it.

Once a snake does attack, its problem is to find an end where it can start swallowing. If its victim is slender, like the lizard opposite, the snake can simply throw its open mouth directly over the creature's head. But if the victim is wriggly and fat, like the rat above, the snake has to immobilize it first, by wrapping coils around it boa-fashion, or—if the snake is poisonous—by giving it a quieting shot of venom.

AN APPARENTLY IMPOSSIBLE TASK confronts the African egg-eater as it opens its mouth to swallow a mountainous-looking egg with a diameter well over twice the width of its own body.

# A Super Swallower

A sure way around the problem of subduing live flesh is to catch it young. The two-foot (61-cm) African snake *Dasypeltis scaber*, shown here, has carried this solution to the ultimate point of eating nothing but birds' eggs, and has become marvelously specialized for this task. Its teeth have dwindled to nubbins which are useful only for gripping a smooth egg. Its jaws are loosely connected to its skull by two swiveling bones which can be dropped down to give *Dasypeltis* the most stretchy mouth of any snake. In its throat are sharp projections sticking down from the backbone and used to rip open eggshells.

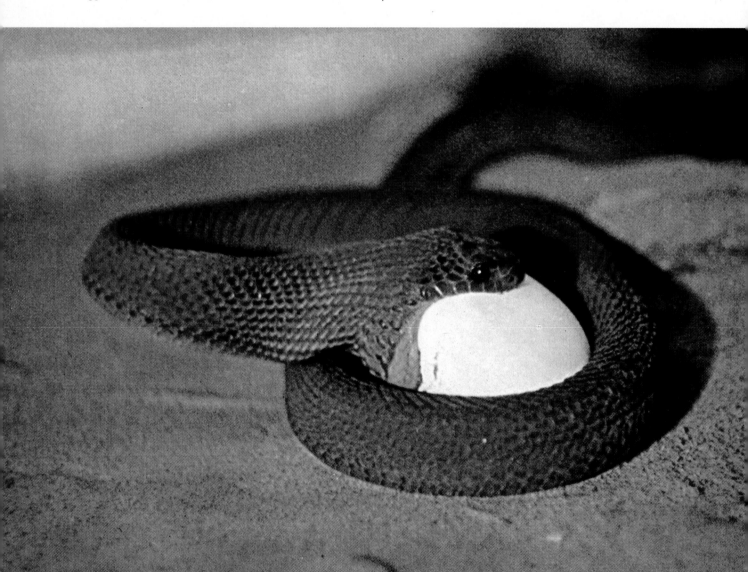

WITH JAWS AT MAXIMUM GAPE, the snake manages to get its mouth around the egg. The pleated lining inside the mouth and the flexible tissues between the jawbones are stretched as far as they will go. The tiny, backward-pointing teeth work their way across the egg's huge smooth dome, and the fountains of the snake's saliva flow freely so that the egg will slide in smoothly.

A valve at the entrance of its stomach will take yolks and whites but will reject pieces of shell. These are regurgitated by special throat muscles that bundle them together, sharp edges in, so that they do not scratch on the way up.

One trouble with an egg diet is that birds lay only in season, and a snake may have to go for a long time without food. Its ability to regurgitate shells is a help here. First, no space inside the snake is wasted on useless materials—if it comes on several eggs it can eat them all. Second, no energy is burned up in passing the shells through the digestive system.

**UP COME THE SHELL FRAGMENTS**, still attached to their underlying membrane, their jagged edges wadded in together. All the nourishing egg fluids have been drained and swallowed.

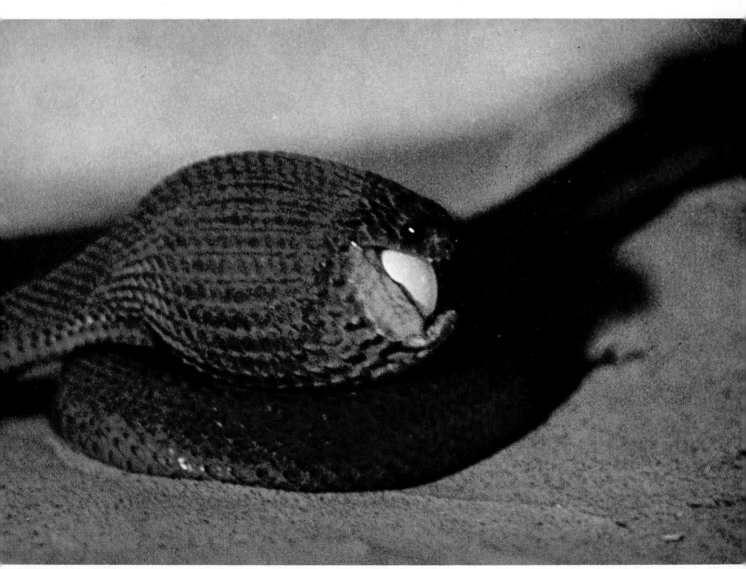

**COMPLETELY INSIDE** the snake's mouth, the egg begins to pass down its elastic throat, where it will come in contact with the sharp internal spines which will break it open. Being roughly spherical, an egg is remarkably resistant to crushing, but once pierced by the spines it will break into small fragments very quickly as it is subjected to muscle spasms of the snake's neck.

# The Infamous Cobra

Although several other species are more deadly, the cobra has the worst reputation of any venomous snake. This is partly because of its large size and fearsome appearance, but mainly because it comes in constant contact with people in crowded Asiatic countries where few have shoes. As a result, it takes about 20,000 lives a year in India alone.

There are 12 species of cobras in the world, spreading from Africa east through southern Asia to the Philippines. Like their close relatives the mambas, the coral snakes and the kraits, they manufacture a mainly neurotoxic venom and eject it through fixed fangs in the front of the upper jaws. These are shorter than the fangs of vipers, and to use them effectively the cobra must resort to grasping and chewing to produce a series of wounds, rather than a single deep stab like a rattler's. Cobras have their own way of advertising their deadliness; they hiss loudly, rear up to a third of their length and spread their necks in the menacing "hood" shown in these pictures.

THE KING COBRA, rare but lethal, can grow to 18 feet (5.5 m). It builds a nest of leaves which it watches until the young hatch, and is regarded by some as the world's most intelligent snake.

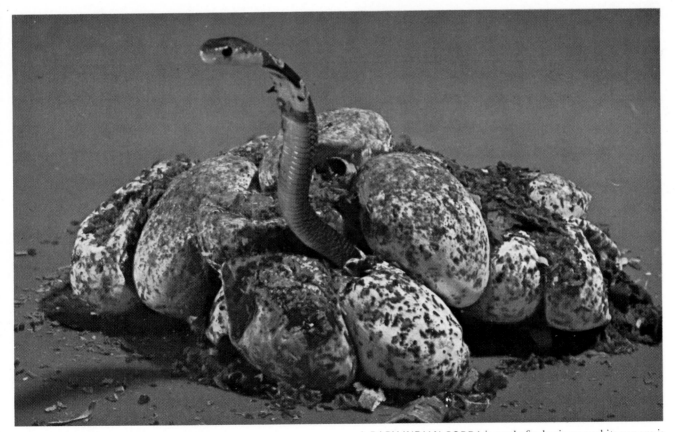

A BABY INDIAN COBRA is ready for business and its venom is as deadly as its parents' from the instant it hatches from its egg. The incubation period for this species is about two months.

THE FEARSOME FACE of a spectacled cobra is actually no face at all but a set of black and white markings on the back of the cobra's neck which it spreads defensively when it is disturbed.

69

SPITTING VENOM, an African black-necked cobra can squirt droplets of liquid with great accuracy for distances of up to eight feet (2.4 m). This is the same stuff that would kill a victim if injected into the blood stream. It is not injurious to the skin, but if it gets in the eyes it produces a burning sensation, and if it is not washed out immediately it can seriously damage the eyes and in some cases even produce blindness. Three species of cobra have the ability to spit, and in all of them it is made possible by the location of the venom hole on the front of the fang, so that when a jet is shot out by the snake it goes forward and upward. There is some evidence that spitting cobras make an instinctive effort to aim directly at the eyes of their enemies.

**THE GAPING STRIKE** of a rattler is revealed stroboscopically at three successive instants as the rattler lunges to sink its fangs into a warm piece of cotton batting. This sequence of laboratory photographs shows that the rattler—though a stabbing viper—can also bite in the ordinary way, with its lower venomless jaws making contact before the fangs administer the *coup de grâce*.

# Fast Fangs of the Rattlers

Experts are constantly being asked: "Are cobras or rattlers the most poisonous?" Traditionally the prize has gone to the cobras, because if white rats are injected with equal amounts of cobra and rattler venom the cobra-injected animal will be the first to die. The true answer, however, is that both are deadly; the choice really depends on whether one prefers to die by paralysis (cobras) or by having one's tissues destroyed (rattlers). But the rattlesnake has it all over the cobra in the efficiency with which it delivers its venom. Its long poison fangs are located far forward in its jaws and are capable of a deep venom-filled stab at the first strike.

THE BLINDFOLD BITE of a rattler with taped eyes aims unerringly at the warm light bulb in a laboratory experiment, guided to the heat through nerves in two special sensory pits in its face.

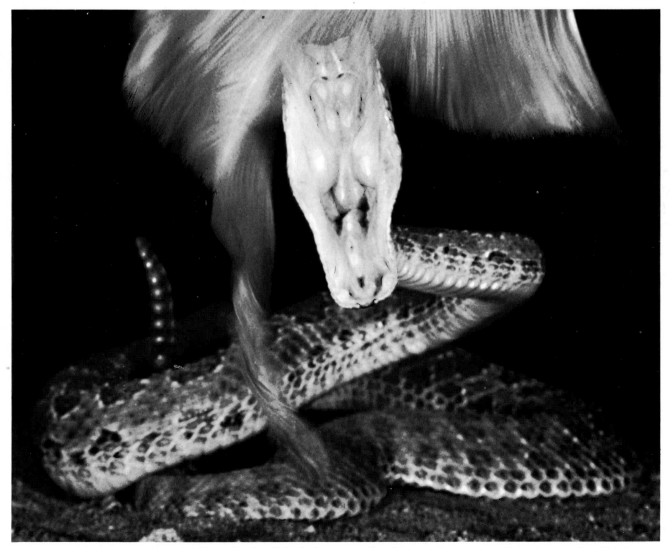

THE STRAIGHT-ON STAB of a rattler is revealed in a light flash triggered by the pop of a balloon bursting under the rattler's jaws. Survival after such a bite depends on the size of the victim and on how much venom gets into the wound, which in turn depends on the size of the snake. Largest doses come from U.S. diamondbacks which can kill a large man in an hour.

PYTHON
(PYTHON RETICULATUS)

ANACONDA
(EUNECTES MURINUS)

BOA
(CONSTRICTOR CONSTRICTOR)

COBRA
(OPHIOPHAGUS HANNAH)

# The Sizes of Some Representative Snakes

Although jungle literature is full of accounts of immense snakes that can swallow animals as big as horses, and although fossil snakes of 50 feet (15.2 m) have been uncovered, the largest snake in the world today is almost certainly under 40 feet (12.2 m). There are reports of 37-foot (11.3-m) South American swamp and river anacondas, but the largest snake ever measured by a scientist was a 33-foot (10.1-m) Asian reticulate python. Thus it receives top billing in this chart of snakes, arranged in order of maximum recorded length and with the largest animals they are known to eat.

The three biggest snake species are all constrictors. Contrary to belief, they do not break a victim's bones and squeeze it to a pulp, but they can and do loop a deer or a goat in several coils in a couple of seconds and squeeze until it suffocates. Large specimens in zoos have put down more than 100 pounds (45 kg) of meat in a single meal, and after such a feast a python is able to go for a year, if nothing else comes along, before eating again. It can and has eaten humans, but they are too often armed or with other humans and go too seldom into the python's haunts to be a key item in its diet. Much more dangerous to men are the large poisonous snakes, notably the king cobra, a record specimen of which measures 18 feet 4 inches (5.6 m). Bushmasters of 12 feet (3.7 m) and rattlers of eight feet (2.4 m) have been caught. DeKay's snake averages a foot (30 cm) in length and can be found in New York's Central Park. But it is not the smallest species. Certain blind snakes are only five inches (12.7 cm) long when mature.

10 (3.0)  5 (1.5)  0

BUSHMASTER
(ESIS MUTA)

BLACK RAT SNAKE
(ELAPHE OBSOLETA)

DIAMONDBACK RATTLESNAKE
(CROTALUS ADAMANTEUS)

RACER
(COLUBER CONSTRICTOR)

KING SNAKE
(LAMPROPELTIS GETULUS)

GARTER SNAKE
(THAMNOPHIS SIRTALIS)

DEKAY'S SNAKE
(STORERIA DEKAY)

STRETCHING HUGELY, a water snake grips a fat toad and accomplishes the seemingly impossible task of swallowing it. In such everyday feats small common snakes duplicate in miniature the prodigious predations of pythons, boas or anacondas.

## Tiny Terrors in the Grass

When man thinks of predators in the reptile world, he is likely to think of the large, dramatic animals like alligators, crocodiles, boas and rattlesnakes—creatures with whom his contacts are relatively rare. But to the small animals of field, forest and stream, it is the little garter snake or water snake that is the enemy, lying in wait in any clump of grass or marshy shoreline. The results of such an encounter are shown here—a swift and merciless struggle, and then the slow process of digestion, one life dissolved so that another may survive.

AN X-RAYED GARTER SNAKE discloses the long journey of a small animal through the snake's sinuous gut. The bulge at left is the carcass of a frog 84 hours after swallowing. The frog's hind limbs are already gone and its spine is beginning to dissolve.

# 4

# The Business of Living

REPTILES are found almost throughout the world. This does not mean that any reptile is likely to turn up in just any old place, or that any particular kind of reptile lives everywhere. It does mean that almost every part of the world is inhabited by reptiles of one kind or another and has something to offer them that they have made use of, be it in the water, the air, on the land or even under the land. Whether you are swimming or walking or climbing trees or digging in the ground, you are liable to encounter some sort of reptile, and you come upon them in every major region of the globe except Antarctica.

More than anywhere else, reptiles prosper and abound in the tropics. That is where most of the reptile families are represented. Some of these tropical families have representatives in the Temperate Zones too, but only two families are peculiar to the cooler regions of earth—a minor group of legless lizards in California and the tuatara on its chill New Zealand islands. Reptiles are not very good at withstanding cold. Only three species reach the Arctic. They seem to be even less able to put up with conditions at high altitudes, and there are almost none of the reptilian class in the highest mountain zones. The distribution of a plant or an animal throughout the world is known as its range.

## TOO MUCH ALIKE
## TO LIVE TOGETHER

*Two lizard families, very similar in their adaptations and closely related, now have separate distributions in the two hemispheres. Iguanids, the older family, are almost entirely restricted to the New World, as shown by the areas of solid color on the top globe. Their counterparts, the agamids, live only in the Old World (lighter areas on bottom globe). It is tempting to speculate that the two families developed independently in their respective hemispheres, except for the fact that a few iguanids linger in isolated parts of the Old World: on Madagascar, and the Fiji and Tonga Islands in the western Pacific. Fossils in England and France have also been tentatively identified as iguanids of some 58 million years ago. Therefore it seems likely that this family was once worldwide, and persists today only where the later agamids have not been able to spread.*

Range means simply the geographic territory occupied. The ranges of reptiles, like those of any creature, are molded by several kinds of factors. Some of these are historical, reflecting the age of the species or group and the geologic events that have occurred in the region occupied. Others are ecological, involving the tolerances and preferences of the creature in question. A close look at the ranges of a number of reptiles—or of animals or plants of any kind—soon reveals that none of them, neither the young new species nor the old complex groups, appear to be occupying all the territory they should be capable of inhabiting. The reasons for this are diverse. Some are obscure, some clearly evident; all are worth thinking about.

Although complicated influences shape the ranges of animals, the fundamental fact is that patterns of distribution have been built, over a period of time, by animals spreading into suitable and accessible territory. Thus, other things being equal, the older a form of life is, the bigger its range will be. But other things are hardly ever equal, and while this principle is a necessary one to know, the conditions under which it alone applies are almost never found. Extraneous factors nearly always complicate the simple fundamental relation between time and spread.

For example, take the legless, blind lizard mentioned in Chapter 1 which I occasionally find when plowing on my farm. This worm lizard of the family Amphisbaenidae is found only in peninsular Florida. In the same region there is a scaly-backed swift, or fence, lizard, the Florida scrub lizard, which is also found nowhere else. These two lizards lead very different lives, but they occupy roughly the same territory—or, to put it differently, their habitats are very different but they have comparable geographic ranges. If the simple relation between time and spread were always applicable, it would follow that these two lizards have about the same background of history and age. Instead, however, they almost certainly originated many millions of years apart. The worm lizard belongs to a shrunken and ancient group with a drastically broken-up distribution which can be traced through a widespread fossil record, but it has today no near relative in Florida or even in continental North America. The scrub lizard, on the other hand, is closely related to other lizards in nearby areas, and may have diverged from them only a few million years ago, perhaps even in the same general area it now occupies.

Is the scrub lizard, then, spreading into new territory? It is not possible to say. In the case of the worm lizard, fossils show that the range of the group to which it belongs has contracted. But whether the Florida species is extending its territory or losing ground is anybody's guess.

Thinking of these two ranges as simple products of time and the ability of the animal to get about would bring one to mistaken conclusions. In any area, accounting for the distribution of each species found there is a demanding problem, and one that requires a careful appraisal of various evolutionary, ecological and paleogeographic events and processes. For every race that survives, many become extinct. Extinction eliminates not just single species, but whole clusters of lines—genera, families, and even orders. Thus the range of an old group nearly always will have been affected by the destructive process of extinction, as well as by the constructive one of spreading.

But in spite of the oddities of their distribution, reptiles are products of evolution—each kind originated in one place only—and for that reason their ranges over the earth do show certain regularities that allow generalizations to be made. One sort of generalization concerns the concentration of certain genera, families or orders of reptiles in particular geographic areas. On the separate continents the different reptile groups are represented in different ways. The spread of the crocodilians is very different from the complicated pattern turtles show. Lizards are distributed in yet another way, and not at all like the snakes, among which boids and colubrids have widely divergent geographic patterns. In most of these cases it is not possible to reconstruct the history—the origin and wanderings—of the group by simply studying its distribution. One of the few cases in which a major group of reptiles can be seen to have spread from a definite and recognizable center of origin is that of the advanced colubrid snakes. The distribution of these reptiles strongly suggests that the Asiatic tropics are their ancestral land.

Another sort of regularity that a survey of the ranges of reptile groups reveals is a tendency for their distribution to correspond, in a general and average kind of way, with that of other plants and animals whose own ranges are more or less different. This is not a matter of exact correspondence of range limits, but rather a broad, global tendency for certain zones to share certain groups of animals and plants which are held there largely by climatic factors, while other types are excluded. Averaging out these correspondences in distribution provides the zoogeographer, whose task it is to study the relation of life to geographical areas, with a set of life regions that makes up a crude but sometimes useful pattern of world distribution of living things. The pattern, to be sure, is too broad to tell much about the individual species which occupy the life regions, but it does tell a good deal about the world as a place for life.

Animals wander and drift and are blown about the globe. Susceptibility to geographic dispersal of any kind has been given a special name: vagility. Any spreading that results in an extension of range is an expression of a creature's vagility. The capacity may or may not have to do with powers of locomotion. Marine animals, birds and stronger-flying insects tend to have bigger ranges than terrestrial species. On the other hand, some of the most delicate insects are distributed worldwide, evidently because they can so readily be transported by currents of air. Some of the most widespread of all animals are feeble creatures such as protozoa or crustacea, which have scarcely any locomotor ability at all, but whose cysts or eggs can be swirled about the world like dust, or carried from place to place in mud stuck on the feet of birds.

In the study of the geographical distribution of animals, the inhabitants of islands are of special interest. The kinds of animals that live on an island are a clue to its past, to its possible connections with land areas in past geologic times. The record of sedimentary rocks is often hidden under water or under other deposits. Geologists, doubtful about the character and scheduling of connections among islands, turn to the distribution of plants, and especially of animals, for guidance. The evidence provided is indirect and often ambiguous or muddled, but it is frequently the best available.

To get trustworthy data from island animals, one has to be able to recognize cases of introduction by man. Geckos, for instance, are inveterate stowaways, and some of them have worked their way all over the tropics by just being on hand when man's cargoes were being shipped around the globe.

To some extent the same qualities that make an animal a good stowaway may qualify it for more natural kinds of overseas dispersal, especially for traveling on rafts. Although there can be little doubt that many of the lizards that are widespread members of island fauna got there across water barriers, the exact method of their transportation is not known. The zoogeographer P. J. Darlington believes that winds have been of little importance in distributing island reptiles. Although this is probably true, the anole lizards, which are slim, light, arboreal and characteristic of island fauna, might be an exception. But for most island reptiles, raft transportation is surely a more important factor.

It is a shame that the distribution of animals by natural rafts has been so little studied. There are various places in the world where much could be learned by direct observation. The south shore of Trinidad, where flood water from the Orinoco brings in all kinds of raftborne waifs, would be a good place to undertake such a project.

## THE ADVANTAGES OF BEING LEGLESS

*Long, skinny and legless, a snake can exploit many parts of a habitat better than most four-footed animals. The garter snake of the eastern United States (above) is ordinarily found on stony hillsides near creeks. Its ground-hugging form allows it to move quickly and silently through crevices, decaying leaves, logs or tall grass. In these places it also finds the amphibians and worms that are its prey.*

In the *Pictorial Museum of Animated Nature*, a 19th Century journal in which many wonders are on view, I came across an old record of reptile-rafting to St. Vincent—an island some 150 miles (241 km) north of Trinidad and downstream from it in the Equatorial Current. The item is quoted from the writings of the Reverend Lansdown Guilding of St. Vincent, and though old and quaint it is a rare sort of observation. It sounds authentic, so I offer it here:

"A noble specimen of the boa constrictor was lately conveyed to us by the currents, twisted round the trunk of a large sound cedar tree which had probably been washed out of the bank by the floods of some great South American river, while its huge folds hung on the branches as it waited for its prey. The monster was fortunately destroyed after killing a few sheep, and his skeleton now hangs before me in my study, putting me in mind how much reason I might have had to fear in my future rambles through St. Vincent, had this formidable reptile been a pregnant female and escaped to a safe retreat."

Thus, if the evidence offered by animals is used to reconstruct paleogeographic history, the vagility of the species involved obviously has to be reckoned in, and here reptiles play a particularly important role. Lizards generally are among the most ubiquitous island animals, and although some of their island range is the work of man, much of it is the result of their special tendencies to passive transportation by natural forces. Amphibians, mammals and snakes, on the other hand, are much less susceptible to interisland distribution than lizards. If an observer were to be suddenly transported to an unknown island and a look around revealed a varied assortment of amphibians, snakes and mammals, for example, he could be confident that the place was not far from a mainland shore and that recent connections had existed. But if there were no snakes at all there, and no mammals or amphibians, but instead the place was swarming with lizards, there would be no doubt that it was a far-off island, and very likely a volcanic one with no land bridges in its recent history.

So while one factor involved in the distribution of animals is the distance to be covered and another is the time that has elapsed, a third consideration is the innate ability of the potential colonist to get across the distance. Still another factor, quite as important as the others, is the ability of the animal to survive in the new place when it gets there. No matter how narrow the barrier, how long the time, or how great the dispersal ability of an animal, its spread will finally be limited by the amount of appropriate habitat. In trying to account for the distribution of the fauna of an area it is often not easy to distinguish between the effects of history and ecology.

The three major media of the world—earth, air and water—have all been repeatedly invaded and exploited by the reptiles in many different ways. Most reptiles live on the surface of the ground or in trees; but they are down with the earthworms too, and they glide and parachute about, and once they even very nobly cruised the air.

There is no modern reptile capable of sustained aerial locomotion. The most advanced aerial reptiles that ever lived, the pterosaurs of the Mesozoic, are all extinct. Though perhaps preeminently soarers or gliders, they were in some cases surely capable of flapping flight, and may even have fed on the wing, like an albatross or a pelican. The other important—and more lasting—aerial venture during the Age of Reptiles was made by the line that became birds.

Although true flight has been lost to the reptile line, there are many arboreal snakes and lizards in which body weight has been drastically cut down, making it possible for them to fall from great heights without injury. I have many times seen little anoles, while courting or fighting in the trees in my yard, fall from 40 or 50 feet (12 to 15 m) up and suffer no evident damage. In fact, they often scurry straightway to the nearest tree and go up it, as if the incident had not even phased them. The light-bodiedness of such tree-climbing reptiles is itself an aerial adaptation that enhances survival by checking acceleration before a dangerous speed of fall is reached. From this to parachuting, by spreading flaps of skin, broadened feet and legs, or the rib-supported edges of the body wall to increase buoyancy, is another step along the same adaptive path, and one that has been taken by various modern lizards and snakes. In some of these—notably *Chrysopelea*, the oriental "flying snake," and the lizards of the genus *Draco*—the broad surfaces are so extensive that the fall actually becomes a long glide and the direction of the flight may even be partially controlled by the gliding animal. The whole line of development from the arboreal habitat to aerial locomotion seems such a clear one that the lack of any recent flying reptile is like an incongruous gap.

THERE are not many kinds of living space from which reptiles are absent. Invasions of the soil, for example, have been made repeatedly by unrelated kinds of snakes and lizards, many of which have lost eyes, legs or both in adapting to a burrowing existence. Three different ways of living underground may be distinguished. One is to dig and inhabit a permanent burrow, as monitors and various other lizards and some tortoises do. In these cases, feeding is not subterraneous. The burrow serves only for concealment or for maintaining a tiny set of favorable weather conditions to retire into when it is bad outside. Another way to go underground is to wriggle into and through loose soil or sand. Such sand-swimming is the habit of various kinds of snakes, and of skinks like the Australian sandfish and the little, nearly legless *Neoseps* of central Florida, and of several other kinds of lizards. The sand viper of African deserts shuffles itself quickly into the sand and, incidentally, leaves the black tip of its tail protruding from the surface as a bait for prey. Like burrowing, sand-swimming is more a way to hide or avoid unfavorable physical factors than a means of locomotion. Sand-swimmers are mainly desert animals, for the not surprising reason that deserts are where the most sand is.

The third way to live underground is to live there all the time. The most confirmed subterranean reptiles are the true underground foragers like the blind, mostly legless, amphisbaenian lizards. This bizarre group has inhabited the soil since the days of the dinosaurs. Most of them stay below permanently, and they evidently travel about over considerable distances, finding their food— mostly worms and insects—in the subterranean habitat. As they move through

## HOW SNAKES MOVE

**SERPENTINE MOVEMENT**

*Of the four principal methods of snake movement, the most familiar is serpentine. The body literally swims along in a series of curves which gain traction from exerting pressure against sticks, exposed roots, grass blades, pebbles or irregularities in the ground. The snake in the diagram above is using some small stones for leverage as it winds forward, and will secure fresh purchases encountering other objects.*

**CONCERTINA MOVEMENT**

*The mechanics of concertina movement are much like those of an inchworm's progress along a branch. At rest the snake's body appears tightly coiled (left). With the tail anchored, the head and neck dart forward (center). Then the neck region grips the ground and the rest of the body is pulled up (right) and again compressed in concertina fashion, in preparation for another fast forward movement of the head.*

the soil, they leave tubelike trails behind them, but no one knows to what extent these are re-used as permanent tunnels or burrows.

Little is known of the natural history of subterraneous reptiles. Some 25 years ago, while digging in my yard, I had the vast luck to disinter two eggs of the Florida worm lizard. They were the first ever seen by anyone, but besides that, they were especially interesting because of their extraordinarily long, almost cylindrical shape, because they contained fully formed embryos ready for hatching, and above all because the little lizards in them had conspicuous black eye-spots, whereas mature Florida worm lizards are without any sign of eyes at all. In looking through the literature on lizard habits recently, I was surprised to see that in all the years since I found those eggs, no more have been seen by anyone—or at least by anyone inclined to tell of them in print.

ONE burning question posed by the extreme privacy of the lives of subterraneous reptiles is how the males find the females at breeding time. As in all reptiles, fertilization is internal, and an interlude of mating must be envisioned. But how does it happen, with each worm lizard inching around deep down in the ground and cut off by cold earth from the sight, sound or smell of a prospective partner? No one knows.

Reptiles are well-represented in the desert. Besides the sand-swimmers, there are many that live under rocks and in crevices. Others live in holes in the ground. Very few of these are underground foragers, however, since in deserts there is very little food, either plant or animal, beneath the surface. Most of them are nocturnal and come to the surface to hunt when the sun goes down, although in some cold deserts the regimen is reversed.

A well-made permanent burrow is a limited bit of favorable environment, and various kinds of interloping creatures often are drawn to it and live there more or less in intimacy and harmony. A classic example is the burrow of the gopher tortoise in the southeastern United States, inhabited quite regularly by rattlesnakes, indigo snakes, two kinds of lizards, the gopher frog, various small mammals and a great many insects. Some of these guests go in merely to elude a pursuer. I have often seen rattlesnakes, indigo snakes and foxes barge forthwith into a burrow in which I knew the turtle to be at home. Abandoned gopher burrows are regularly taken over by various mammals as dens. But many occupants of gopher holes—notably some insects and the gopher frog—are true guests, which live intimately with the turtle and have evidently worked out satisfactory ways to keep from being trampled by his comings and goings.

Other reptiles habitually occupy the burrows of various other kinds of animals. Ant galleries and termite nests have special snake and lizard guests. On the dry Pacific slope of Central America much of the reptile fauna can be found at one time or another enjoying the hospitality offered by the burrows of tarantulas, leaf-cutting ants or armadillos.

The range of an animal can be shown on a map. Its habitat cannot. You can plot the distribution of the sort of topography or vegetation or climate in which an animal may be expected to occur, but this would show little about the character of the habitat. A habitat is a place; but it is also the sum of the conditions that make the place easy or hard to live in. These conditions are partly physical and partly biological. Some can readily be seen or measured, but some of them are subtle or hidden.

In the physical environment of the land one of the clear-cut problems encountered by reptiles, whose ancestors came out of the water, was the danger of drying up. It was this danger that was behind the evolution of the famous shelled reptilian egg, and the same danger imposed the selective pressures that brought changes in the body of the animal itself. It caused reptiles to evolve a horny epidermal covering to cut down evaporation of their body water. This covering, laid on in the form of scales or plates, does not prevent all loss of water. A reptile is perfectly capable of drying up, but the scales do slow down the process to the point where reptiles are able to live in the driest places on earth if they live carefully. The epidermal layer is periodically shed. In snakes and in a few lizards it tends to come off in one piece, the cast skin faithfully reproducing the surface sculpturing of the animal's body, even down to the spectacle over the eyes. In other lizards the skin comes off in patches. In some kinds of turtles the horny scales of the shell surface fall off, but in others they pile up, and unless worn away show peripheral growth rings. In regions with well-marked seasons these rings may be of some value to researchers in determining the age of the turtle.

As reptiles pioneered in dry places it was not just the danger of desiccation that they faced. Another big change that fairly slapped them in the face was the wild and capricious temperature regimen of the land. By contrast, water, with its steady daily and yearly temperature cycles, is an easy, even environment. Besides the need to guard against loss of body water the new reptiles had to work out a way to combat the vicissitudes of heat and cold ashore. A long time later their descendants, the birds and mammals, were to do this by balancing high production of metabolic heat with clever radiating devices; but no living reptile is yet able to control its body temperature in this way. For a long time zoologists supposed that reptiles had no control at all over the body temperature, and that it helplessly rose and fell with that of the surroundings. Reptiles were, and until lately have been, spoken of as "cold-blooded" animals.

Now, primarily because of some shrewd researches of R. B. Cowles and Charles Bogert, carried out during the 1940s, this idea has had to be abandoned. Reptiles are not at the mercy of the temperature of the milieu. If they were, they would get very little done, even by reptilian standards. Actually they can maintain a fair control over their blood temperature, and they do this not by controlling gain or loss of metabolic heat, but by moving around, by alternately seeking and avoiding sunlight or warm ground. They practice what is called behavioral temperature control, and some species, at least, maintain their preferred temperature at a remarkably steady level. Not much is known about temperatures in nonbasking reptiles, such as those nocturnal or forest species that would seem shut off from any heat sources except the air or water around them. But the studies of Cowles and Bogert have provided the groundwork for a greatly broadened concept of the habitat of the terrestrial reptile.

Temperature and humidity are only two in a complex system of physical factors that a reptile has to reckon with—to tolerate, to seek or to escape from as it lives out its life. Even if we knew all about all these we would still not know very much about the habitat of the animal, because many of the important characteristics of the habitat—its demands and opportunities—are determined by the living things that share it with the creature one has in mind. Even animals and plants that only very briefly enter the range of a reptile's activities may alter living conditions there.

The most obvious kind of communion between living beings of separate kinds is the predator-prey relation. The hog-nosed snake eats a toad and is eaten by

**SIDEWINDING**

*The best way to visualize the looping movement of the sidewinder in sand is to imagine a piece of wire coiled into slightly less than two loops and then rolled along the sand—it will make a series of unconnected oblique tracks like the three in the diagram above. That is what the sidewinder does; it touches the ground at only two points (shown in color) and unrolls its body along the dotted track until its head is extended enough to touch down for the beginning of another loop.*

**CATERPILLAR CRAWL**

*Large, heavy-bodied snakes like the constrictors often crawl straight ahead, leaving a track resembling that of a dragged rope. To achieve this motion, the broad, flat belly scales are slid forward. They catch the ground like tractor treads, and allow the rest of the body to be pulled up to them. This action may occur alternately at several points along the snake's body, and is shown in color in these drawings.*

a king snake. A monitor lizard eats the eggs of a crocodile and then one day is itself eaten by the crocodile that laid the eggs. Of 10,000 sea turtles that hatch on a beach maybe 10, maybe 100 escape bird and mammal predators on the shore and fishes waiting beyond the surf. Such violent interplay among living things is important, but other less violent relationships are perhaps equally so. There are diverse kinds and shades of advantageous contacts, not only among the members of a single species, but also among the various species that share a living place. In the case of every reptile, some time is spent by the sexes in finding one another, courting and mating. Snakes gather for hibernation, turtles mass for migration and breeding, and in each case the function is furthered by the grouping. On the other hand, sharing foraging territory invites combat and strife, so we find that snakes and lizards, and evidently crocodilians and turtles too, tend to stake out, and more or less actively defend as their own, parcels of the habitat. Except for the sexual and territorial behavior of a few species, the whole subject of sociality in reptiles has not been adequately investigated, but enough is known to suggest that there is much to be learned about it.

Just as the individual comes into repeated contact with others of its kind, so the species is always involved in the lives of other species. Most reptiles are carnivorous, and are therefore deeply involved in predator-prey exchanges in their habitats. As has been shown, this brings about various sorts of adaptations that help them to escape being eaten as well as to capture and eat other creatures. Little is known about the more subtle roles and relations of reptiles in their biological environments. They are hosts to various parasites, but none of them lives parasitically. There are lizards and snakes that live exclusively in termite and ant nests, however, and are thus to some extent social parasites. There are not many known cases of beneficial mutualism among reptiles, of useful partnerships between species, although it is likely that more knowledge of the natural history of the group will reveal many cases of casual partnerships and dependencies that are being overlooked now.

Some of the best evidence of the rapport of reptiles with their surroundings is to be seen in the deceptive behavior and resemblances they have evolved. The commonest of these are protective colors, patterns or shapes. The same species may be dark-colored on dark soil and light where light background predominates. Some reptiles—most notably the chameleon—are able to manipulate their coloration to conform to or blend with different surroundings. The most elaborate concealing equipment combines coloration and form, as in three genera of Old World geckos that have greatly flattened bodies and tails, and barklike color patterns. Behavior is often modified to reinforce deceptive resemblances. Various snakes, such as the South American vine snake *Oxybelis*, both look and act like inanimate twigs, vines or lianas. One of these even falls to the ground when touched and lies there like a dead twig. Still other kinds of snakes, including some of the coral snakes and some of the snakes that look like them, manipulate the hind end of the body with considerable verisimilitude as if it were the head end—a maneuver seemingly designed to divert attention from the more vulnerable part.

Along with warning coloration or behavior, some reptiles have developed an ability to mimic warning devices, even though they have no dangerous or unpleasant properties of their own. Some biologists do not believe in the reality of many cases of mimicry. Partly this is because of the lack of laboratory proof of the phenomenon; partly it is because some people lean so far backward to avoid anthropocentric judgments that they fall clear over; and partly the skepticism has been fomented by some real errors of judgment that proponents of the mimicry idea have committed.

For example, I have heard it said that harmless snakes mimic rattlesnakes by vibrating their tails in dry leaves. As Chapter 3 divulged, it is true that many kinds of harmless snakes do vibrate their tails when approached by a potential enemy. But in this particular case, what they do cannot possibly be regarded as mimicry. The wide distribution of the trait suggests that snakes were vibrating their tails to scare off enemies long before there were any rattlesnakes in the world. So what rattlesnakes have done is simply to refine and elaborate an adaptation already entrenched in various snake lines. To be sure, some reinforcement of the widespread tail-shaking habit may occur in snakes living in rattlesnake territory, if only because the rattlesnakes buzz so well and because they back up the warning with such deadly effect. But to think that a black snake is mimicking a rattlesnake when it vibrates its tail is to miss an important point.

ONE of the sources of controversy is the anthropocentric sound of the word mimicry. The verb "to mimic" seems to some people to carry a taint of volition, and this colors their appraisal of alleged cases of mimicry and makes them suspicious that these are figments of nonobjective interpretation of nature. One of the controversial cases in which even herpetologists are split into camps is that of the so-called mimicking of the gaudily ringed, poisonous American coral snakes by various harmless species. Although often referred to as mimicry, these resemblances are regarded by some zoologists as examples of convergent evolution, in which the coral snakes and their nonpoisonous counterparts have developed similar color patterns for some utilitarian reason not connected with

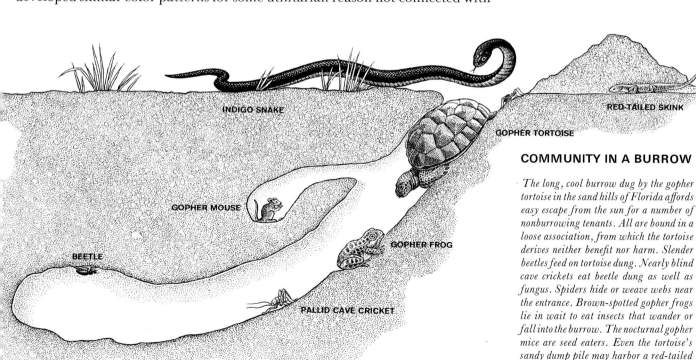

INDIGO SNAKE

RED-TAILED SKINK

GOPHER TORTOISE

GOPHER MOUSE

GOPHER FROG

BEETLE

PALLID CAVE CRICKET

## COMMUNITY IN A BURROW

*The long, cool burrow dug by the gopher tortoise in the sand hills of Florida affords easy escape from the sun for a number of nonburrowing tenants. All are bound in a loose association, from which the tortoise derives neither benefit nor harm. Slender beetles feed on tortoise dung. Nearly blind cave crickets eat beetle dung as well as fungus. Spiders hide or weave webs near the entrance. Brown-spotted gopher frogs lie in wait to eat insects that wander or fall into the burrow. The nocturnal gopher mice are seed eaters. Even the tortoise's sandy dump pile may harbor a red-tailed skink. Sometimes the gopher tortoise defends its burrow against a snake predator by blocking the entrance with its shell.*

warning at all. Some even say that the duplication of pattern is simple coinci-
dence. To support this view it is pointed out that most mammal predators of
snakes are color blind, and would evidently not be able to see the ringed pattern
as a particularly striking decoration. Moreover, the candystick snakes are all
partly subterraneous, spending most of their time beneath logs, in old stumps or
actually underground, where little seeing is done by anybody. Still another
objection is the occurrence of the ringed coral-snake pattern in harmless snakes
living in places where there are no poisonous models around, and hence no
conceivable advantage to the deception.

The proponents of the mimicry idea are not persuaded by these objections.
They outline their case thus:

(1) There is such a phenomenon as warning coloration. It is widespread
among poisonous species, and occurs in animals as dissimilar as frogs, butter-
flies and the Gila monster. To assume that the poisonous coral snakes are not
exhibiting the phenomenon is less acceptable than to say they are.

(2) Although most of both the poisonous and nonpoisonous candystick snakes
are indeed secretive and addicted to twilight, none is either wholly subterraneous or truly nocturnal; and in any case the time when they are most in danger
of being preyed upon is the interludes when they emerge to the surface, where
the color pattern would be in evidence.

(3) Although some snake predators are color blind, others are not.

(4) If coral snakes get any shred of immunity out of being banded with
gaudy colors, then, by common sense, this immunity is being shared by the
similarly marked scarlet snake and scarlet king snake of the southeastern
United States, and by the host of mimics among harmless snakes of the American tropics—at least in areas where a range is shared by a model and a mimic.
That some places have "mimics" without models (parts of the United States
do, for example) means simply that ranges of animals change through short
spaces of geologic time, while color patterns might be expected to persist for a
while after their utility has gone.

Or how about this, the mimicry school proposes: The red-shouldered hawk
gets about widely, and eats snakes everywhere it goes. If it is one of the predators that instinctively shuns ringed snakes because in some places catching
them is dangerous, then might not the same hawk be expected to shun the
same pattern in other localities, whether or not any penalty were ever imposed
in those places? And so the arguments go on and on.

THESE are some of the most fascinating problems in the field of zoology.
They are crying to be studied experimentally, because that is the only way
some of the questions involved will ever be answered. And what is worse, so
long as they have not been given the glamor of experimental science they will
continue to be deprecated by a lot of bright and otherwise sound scientists who
ought to be studying them. The whole subject of deceptive simulations, including related behavioral adaptations like bluffing and playing dead, is so broad
that it would merit a book to itself. In the single class, Reptilia, there are
myriad examples of this one kind of adaptation. They have all come about
because they impart increased ability to survive. They are signs of the reality
and subtlety of the ecological bonds by which all naturally living beings on
earth are drawn into an exquisitely integrated organization. They are still
another kind of proof that the habitat is more than simply a living space and
that no creature in the world ever lives alone.

HUGE EYES, BIZARRE TAIL AND COLORFUL MARKINGS DISTINGUISH THE KIDNEY-TAILED GECKO, A NOCTURNAL INSECT EATER FROM AUSTRALIA

# Shaped for Survival

Few creatures have taken to the land with the wholehearted enthusiasm of the reptiles. In desert and jungle, in treetop and burrow and cave they found opportunities for living and exploited them all. This, in turn, led to an extraordinary variety of adaptations—night-seeing eyes like the gecko's above, shapes that hide them, feet to carry them anywhere, even shooting tongues to capture prey.

CHUCKWALLA

SIDE-BLOTCHED LIZARD

GILA MONSTER

SPI

WESTERN DIAMONDBACK RATTLESNAKE

Melbourne Brindle

## The Problem of Heat— and How to Make Use of It

Since its body heat depends almost entirely on outside temperature, the "cold-blooded" reptile would seem to be at the mercy of its environment. Actually, by alternately seeking warmer or cooler areas as needed, a reptile keeps its temperature within the range at which it operates best. This painting shows how

90

SIDEWINDER

FRINGE-TOED SAND LIZARD

HORNED LIZARD

DESERT IGUANA

CALIFORNIA GLOSSY SNAKE

LEOPARD LIZARD

various Arizona desert reptiles have conquered the fierce heat. The diamondback rattler avoids the sun by lying in a burrow, while the glossy snake buries itself. The leopard lizard, however, hides to escape Gila monsters. Partially digging in, the sidewinder, horned lizard and sand lizard absorb heat from the sand while shielding parts of their bodies from the sun. The other lizards shuttle between sun and shade, and bask at various angles and on various surfaces in an effort to maintain optimum temperatures. The red racer, with a higher heat tolerance, pursues another vital activity—running down food.

A LEAF-TAILED GECKO from Madagascar shows color and markings which blend almost perfectly with the bark and lichen on the tree trunk to which it clings, a disappearing act enhanced by its leaf-shaped tail and the irregular fringes along its flanks. A large and cosmopolitan tribe, geckos are particularly likable for their chirping voices, whose sound is echoed in their name.

A THREE-HORNED JACKSON'S CHAMELEON FROM EAST AFRICA BASKS ON A BRANCH, UNAWARE OF A LATH SHADING ITS BODY

THE LATH REMOVED, THE CHAMELEON SHOWS A BRIGHT-GREEN BAND, DEMONSTRATING THE EFFECT OF HEAT AND LIGHT ON SKIN COLOR

# Specialists in the Art of Camouflage

Against the rough bark of the tree on the opposite page a gecko is almost invisible—a striking illustration of how the skin colors of many lizards match their backgrounds. Others can go even further, enhancing the effectiveness of their scaly and irregular shapes by means of dark-brown pigment cells which turn the skin lighter or darker as needed. Chameleons can even change color from gray to brown and green, and sometimes even yellow, in response to various stimuli. The East African chameleon seen above demonstrates its reaction to the changes in heat and light produced by a shadow; others show various hues from night to day, or when angered or alarmed. Lizards are the acknowledged masters of such color-changing. Some snakes have the ability, but use it only rarely and in a minor way.

93

ON THE ALERT, THE CHAMELEON SWIVELS ITS TURRETED EYES IN EVERY DIRECTION, OFTEN MOVING EACH INDEPENDENTLY OF THE OTHER

## Varied Eyes for Varied Lives

Reflecting many different ways of life, the eyes of reptiles show an extremely wide range of adaptations and modifications. For example, the burrowing worm lizard, with little need for any vision at all, has vestigial eyes that appear only as a pair of tiny dots in the skin. But to the chameleon, keen vision is vital for survival, and its eyes are unique in a number of ways. Set on the tips of conical turrets projecting from the sides of the head and protected by eyelids which close to tiny peepholes, they are high-

**IN STRONG LIGHT** the vertical pupil of the alligator's eye closes to a slit, much like the pupil of a cat's eye. Unlike a cat, however, the alligator's pupil slit appears colorless in the daylight because the backing of its retina is white. But at night (*opposite*) a dramatic change takes place.

94

SPOTTING ITS PREY, THE CHAMELEON AIMS BOTH EYES FORWARD, BRINGING BINOCULAR VISION INTO PLAY TO GET ITS VICTIM'S RANGE

ly maneuverable, capable of either independent or coordinated movement and matchless in estimating distances for the chameleon's swift-shooting tongue. Night-prowling reptiles like the alligator, on the other hand, have eyes which are well adapted for seeing in the dark. Geckos show an elaborate refinement for light control. Their vertical pupils have notched edges, which can be brought together to form a series of tiny pinholes. Their separate images are then superimposed at the back of the eyeball.

IN DARKNESS the alligator's eye glows rosy-pink, a color often attributed to blood lust. Actually, this is the color of a pigment, rhodopsin, which makes night vision possible. Bleached out by daylight, the pigment imparts an eery glow to light reflected from the retina at night.

ROWS OF SPINY SCALES on the toes of its hind feet enable the fringe-toed lizard to travel quickly and easily over loose sand. Inhabiting desert areas of the southwestern United States, this reptile also uses its specialized feet to dig in and bury itself.

# Feet Which Will Go Anywhere

Carrying their heavy shelters around with them, turtles have no need for speed. Their requirement is for powerful legs able to carry the extra weight and propel them along at a deliberate pace. Most lizards, by comparison, scurry through life at a breakneck clip. Generally, they use all four legs in moving about, but several can run on their hind legs, like man. The majority of them rely on swiftness and agility to capture prey or escape enemies. Thus, depending on where they live, they have feet adapted for running across soft sand or over rocks or for climbing trees. Arboreal species have by far the most specialized feet: The chameleons have opposable toes which grasp branches like pincers, the geckos have marvelous clinging pads. The snakes, on the other hand, have learned how to move about without any legs at all.

PILLAR-LIKE LEGS support the weight of the giant Galápagos tortoise, which sometimes weighs 400 pounds (181 kg) or more. While land turtles have developed short, thick legs, often with sharp claws for digging, marine turtles have evolved flippers.

CLINGING PADS on the undersides of a gecko's toes allow it to scurry easily up trees and smooth walls and even dash across ceilings. The pads, present in most gecko species, consist of a series of plates which are equipped with many tiny hooklike cells.

**TESTING THE AIR,** a sidewinder *(above)* flicks its tongue rapidly to pick up microscopic particles for analysis by its Jacobson's organ, a special sensory apparatus aiding its sense of smell.

**CLEARING ITS VISION,** an Australian naked-toed gecko reaches up with its tongue to wipe the "spectacle" over its eye. More normally, its tongue is also used to pick up and swallow food.

# The Many Uses of Reptiles' Tongues

The flicking tongue of a snake, like that of the sidewinder opposite, is as familiar a part of its popular image as its sinuous leglessness; and indeed, the tongue plays an important role in reptiles' lives. Turtles and crocodilians have fairly simple tongues, however in snakes they are highly modified for two particular services. Forked at the end, they flick rapidly in and out, "sipping" or sampling chemical particles in the air or on the ground, which they then transport to Jacobson's organ, a special chemoreceptor which is not quite for smelling, not quite for tasting, perhaps a little of both. Thus the tongue helps a snake to trail its prey, sample food, sometimes to locate mates. Some rattlers also use it as a warning device, brandishing it stiffly at enemies.

Lizards, by contrast, have unforked tongues which they generally put to the more prosaic uses of picking up, tasting and swallowing food. Some geckos may use their tongues much like windshield wipers, clearing dirt off the transparent coverings of their eyes like the one opposite below, and chameleons employ them in the most dramatic fashion of all, to shoot, immobilize and haul in prey.

**TAKING AIM** on a fly, a chameleon shoots out its long sticky tongue and scores a bull's-eye. The prehensile tail and tonglike toes keep it firmly anchored. When it is not in use the tongue is bunched up in the throat.

## Fancy Footwork without Feet

Evolving from lizards, snakes took an extraordinary course in the matter of locomotion: They developed efficient ways of moving about without any legs at all. Generally they are able to accomplish this in the familiar wavy, or "serpentine," fashion of thrusting sideways with the body, much as a fish swims, with the plates or scales on their undersides finding a purchase against irregularities on the ground (if there are no such rough spots, as on a pane of glass, they cannot move at all). Sometimes, however, snakes glide forward in a straight line—in this case hunching themselves along like caterpillars. Sidewinders hurl themselves ahead in a complicated but efficient fashion by throwing out successive loops diagonally forward. In tree-dwelling species, like the one shown here, the ventral scales are stiffened by transverse keels which give added traction on rough bark surfaces. Bridging a gap from one branch to another, the snake contracts the muscles along the length of its entire body, thus giving it the rigidity of a beam.

LOOSENING ITS COILS, a blunt-headed tree snake prepares to leave the broken end of one branch and bridge the gap to another. Keeled ventral plates and tightly curled tail anchor it firmly.

2. LEVERING THE STIFFENED FORWARD PART OF ITS BODY UPWARD ON ITS COILS, THE SNAKE WINS A PURCHASE ON A HIGHER LIMB

**1.** TIGHTENING ITS MUSCLES TO ACHIEVE RIGIDITY, THE TREE SNAKE STRETCHES OUT TOWARD THE DISTANT BRANCH WHILE UNCOILING

**3.** GLIDING FORWARD, IT TAKES IN SLACK BEFORE UNWINDING THE REST OF ITS BODY AND PULLING IT UP FROM ITS FORMER ANCHORAGE

PEELING OFF its old skin, a hog-nosed snake turns the loosened layer inside out by rubbing it against the ground. About a third of the skin has been shed; the head covering is visible at the second bend at right.

## How Snakes Shed Their Skins

Alone among all vertebrates, snakes go through the periodic process of shedding outgrown skin in one elegantly complete operation: When the time comes, they crawl out of the old skin, usually leaving it intact behind. They can do this because they have no limbs or other projections which might inhibit the shedding, and because their outer covering is literally a one-piece suit, from the "spectacles" covering their eyes to the tips of their tapered tails. The process starts a few days before the actual shedding. The snake's skin takes on a dull and lifeless appearance and its eyes cloud over. It also loses its appetite and tends to become irritable. Many species seek water to soak themselves at this time, since they lose a good deal of body liquid along with the old skin. The actual shedding begins when the snake loosens the skin around its lips by rubbing its mouth against a rough surface. This accomplished, it proceeds to work the skin back over its head. Inch by inch, as the snake crawls through brush and over rocks, the thin outer layer is peeled off inside out like a glove. Finally, often in as little as a half-hour, the snake is completely free of its old skin. Resplendent in fresh colors and glistening new scales, it goes on its way, to repeat the process one to six months later when the new skin is outworn.

OPERATION COMPLETED, the snake gleams in its new coat, its body swollen with alarm at being disturbed by the photographer. The dead skin behind it is now attached only by a small section at the tail.

A GROTESQUE MASK, the translucent head part of a cast snakeskin faithfully reproduces each scale and feature of the living snake's head. The creature even sheds its eye coverings along with the sheath of skin.

THE REAR LEGS of an alligator, clearly revealed in this photograph of a swimming specimen, are longer than its front ones, indicating that the crocodilians' land-dwelling ancestors once walked upright.

# 5

# Return to the Water

SOMEWHERE in my early schooling, and repeatedly here and there with the passing years, I have heard the grave pronouncement that evolution never reverses itself. I don't know just what this means; but whatever it means, it makes no sense. Evolution may very well "reverse itself," either in hidden biochemical ways or in long-term direction. The statistical odds against a rattlesnake's ever becoming one of the particular fishes in its ancestral background are very great, but there is no rule against the occurrence; and returns and reversals in broad, general trends are common. The loss of legs by reptiles, of which I have spoken at length in other chapters, is an example. Another is the return of land animals to water.

One of the dramatic steps in the evolution of vertebrate animals was the reptiles' shaking free of the water and invading the land. Another important evolutionary advance that reptiles have made, not once but many times, has been to go back to the water again. Calling this an advance sounds like a paradox, a caprice that the newcomer thinking about reptiles is likely to want to have explained. And the explanation is not likely to be of much comfort to him, because the answer is that the returning creatures found advantage in the return, and

## SHAPED BY THE SEA

ICHTHYOSAUR

*These illustrations of the ichthyosaur (above), an extinct aquatic reptile of some 200 million years ago, and the modern porpoise (below), a marine mammal, show how the environment can shape members of totally different classes into creatures that look very much alike. When the land-dwelling ancestors of these animals went back to the sea, they developed missile-shaped bodies and fishlike fins and tails. Their backbones, no longer required to support a heavy frame, became more flexible, and their pelvic bones almost disappeared.*

PORPOISE

ways to increase their chances of survival; and that is exactly what attracted them to the land to start with.

Of the three groups of land vertebrates, all have made repeated returns to the ancestral environment. They have gone back to both the sea and fresh water, and their aquatic adaptations range all the way from acquiring a taste for fish to a drastic reforming of the contours, appendages and physiology of their bodies. Although the fossil record is too clouded to tell a great deal about the habitats of ancestral reptiles, it is clear that some of the aquatic reconversions took place at the very beginning of reptile history, while others were made after long periods of specialized living on shore.

There is no doubt that animal life began in the water. Water is the main stuff of protoplasm and it holds in solution most of the other ingredients for life. But besides its suitability as a medium for the primordial chemistry of organic evolution, water has other features that make it continuingly attractive as an environment for the four-footed land animals that left it 300 million years ago.

ONE of these is the stability of its climate. For aquatic animals there is, of course, no evaporation problem at all, and temperature changes, both periodic and sporadic, are far less extreme and rapid than those of the land. Big shifts in atmospheric weather make a slight impression on the weather in the water. The temperature of a lake may change only five degrees (2.8° C.) in a day during which the temperature of the air is changing 30 degrees (16.7° C.). In peninsular Florida it takes several very cold days to bring the water down to 72° F. (22.2° C.) along the gulf coast. The green turtles go on grazing on the flats there long after the skinks in the inland hammocks have gone into hibernation.

The density of water, as compared to that of air, is another of its important qualities as an environment. Much of a land animal's architecture goes into structure for mechanical support, and the larger the animal, the firmer this support must be. Thus, animals that live entirely on land cannot grow much bigger than modern elephants. The huge dinosaurs probably spent a good deal of time standing or wallowing about in swamps, relying on the buoying power of water to ease the burden on their bones. A hippopotamus does the same thing today. In water, considerations of support impose no limits on size—as is shown by giant whales and squids, and by jellyfish that weigh several hundred pounds. Even today, when reptiles are relatively small, there are some pretty ponderous beasts among marine turtles and crocodilians.

The same factor that makes vast size possible in water imposes a strong limit on speed. To get about slowly in water is easy. But to cruise the open water requires a drastic remodeling of the terrestrial body. It demands streamlining, and even then speeds cannot approach those of birds in air, or of the fastest land animals. Water reptiles have adapted their locomotion in various ways, ranging from the fishlike swimming of the extinct ichthyosaurs and the undulations of snakes, crocodilians and lizards, to a variety of paddling techniques.

One fundamental problem reptiles face in the water is respiration. Most water has oxygen dissolved in it, but a lung cannot extract this; and evolving a gill necessitates a complex remodeling of the circulatory system. No reptile has real gills. Some kinds, however, have converted body surfaces to extract small amounts of oxygen from water, and thus can prolong their dives. Some turtles, for instance, appear to get oxygen through the membranes of the pharynx and cloaca, and probably through the skin. Southern musk turtles may augment aquatic respiration this way, or even dispense with it completely by using energy generated from an oxygenless breakdown of the animal starch, glycogen.

One advantage of the aquatic environment is the ease and impunity with which it allows a water animal to urinate. This may sound like a trivial matter but it is not. The life processes of animals produce ammonia as a waste, and this becomes poisonous if it accumulates in the body. The ammonia can be converted to urea, which is less toxic, and stored for a longer time without harmful effect, but eventually it must be voided. For aquatic animals this is no problem, because both urea and ammonia are soluble, and can be carried away by simply flushing them out; this is a use of water that reptiles in some land habitats could not afford. Some land reptiles that have to conserve water—such as tortoises, snakes and lizards—convert their nitrogenous waste to a semisolid state and eliminate it with the feces, as birds do. To aquatic turtles and crocodilians, however, conservation of water is no problem, and they prodigally flush away ammonia or urea or both. Although it may never be known for sure, the ichthyosaurs, plesiosaurs and other wholly marine reptiles very likely did the same.

This intake of surrounding water, however, does present problems for reptiles that live in salt water. To survive, they must quickly remove from their tissues the great amounts of salt ingested. The kidney, the skin and the respiratory tract can eliminate most of it, but some marine reptiles have evolved a salt gland, which concentrates body salt for elimination. It appears in sea snakes, in sea turtles, including the estuarine diamondback terrapin, and in many lizards. In snakes it is located beneath the tongue, and salty fluid is spit out whenever the tongue is extended. Lizards have the gland near their nostrils, and sneeze out the salty excretion; turtles have it behind their eyes, and weep salty tears.

Finally, the reptile that commits itself completely to living in the water is faced with the need to make some important adjustments in its methods of reproduction. Reptile eggs drown as readily as the animal that lays them. The two recourses here have been going back ashore to lay the eggs, and bearing live young that are ready to swim and to come up for air.

By far the most complete conversion to aquatic life that any reptile ever made was that of the ichthyosaurs. These creatures appeared in the Triassic, reached a peak of abundance and diversity in the Jurassic, and unaccountably disappeared during the latter part of the Cretaceous, when other marine reptiles were still well represented. The ichthyosaur probably lived much as the smaller toothed whales and porpoises live today. Its body was fishlike and drastically molded for swimming, short and torpedo-shaped with a high dorsal fin. The limbs it used on land had become lateral fins. The number of toe bones was greatly increased. Whenever four-footed reptiles or mammals return to the water and become highly modified for aquatic locomotion, they show this increase in the number of toe bones—not in toes, but in the joints of the toes. The bones multiply, shorten and crowd closely together as supports for the guiding plane or paddle that the limb has become. There is little motion between the separate bones—a paddle is no good if it is too floppy. The flexibility they allow is just enough to make a maneuverable surface for propulsion or steering. The ichthyosaurs are the only aquatic tetrapods in which, besides this increase in toe bones, the number of toes themselves has increased, additional ones having been laid down beside the fundamental five that the creature took with it when it entered the sea. As in fishes and dolphins, the neck was short and stiff and the propulsive force of the body was abetted by that of the powerful tail. This resembled the tail of a modern-day shark, except that the tip of the backbone turned down into the lower, rather than toward the upper, lobe of the fin. The ichthyosaurs were obviously true marine animals. Many of them may have led a completely pelagic life, and would no doubt have been as helpless on shore as any porpoise or marlin is today.

This makes one wonder how ichthyosaurs reproduced, because they certainly took the reptilian egg into the water with them, and no reptilian egg can withstand immersion. The answer evidently is that ichthyosaurs bore living young. This is not only a logical assumption because of the occurrence of viviparous species among modern reptiles, but it is also borne out by the fossil record. In the black shales of Bavaria, skeletons of pregnant female ichthyosaurs have actually been found. It is too late to find out, but I wonder if a mother ichthyosaur went through the elaborate postpartum behavior that a porpoise does, boosting her newborn young to the top of the water to take its first breaths of air.

THE typical ichthyosaur mouth was the usual fish-trap style of jaw—long and slender with many small teeth. Some were toothless, however, and in others the lower jaw was undershot like that of a swordfish.

Besides the interest they hold as the most aquatic reptiles that ever lived, the ichthyosaurs confront paleontologists with two great mysteries. One of these is their strange disappearance during the very heyday of marine reptiles. Although they lived the lives now lived by whales, they were certainly not displaced by their mammalian counterparts, the rise of which came millions of years later. The other thing nobody has ever been able to ascertain about ichthyosaurs is what major reptile group they came from. Some of the older ichthyosaur fossils are a bit more primitive than those of the burgeoning Jurassic stocks, but none gives any clue as to the origin of this reptilian line.

Another strain of marine reptiles that became adapted to the water in an extraordinary way was the plesiosaurs of the Jurassic and Cretaceous. Plesiosaurs had broad, flattened bodies like shell-less turtles, powerful paddle-like limbs and rather short, finless tails. In some the neck was so long that the animal has been described as a snake threaded through a turtle. They evidently ate fish, but their fishing technique was clearly different from that of the long-jawed, short-necked, many-toothed, fish-eating animals. Old reconstructions of plesiosaurs showed the neck as flexible and swanlike. It is easy to imagine that the animal fed by darting movements of its head, by which it plucked fishes from

## SOME COMMON AMERICAN TURTLES

*Compared to the giant sea turtles, which weigh hundreds of kilograms, the common American turtles shown here are relatively small, running from several grams to a few kilograms. The soft-shelled turtle, an aquatic genus, is found in the central and eastern states. Although it spends much time concealing itself in river bottoms, paradoxically it is also fond of basking in the sun. The spotted turtle, easily recognized by the yellow spots on its shell, is semiaquatic and lives in the ditches and muddy streams of the East and Midwest.*

*The common mud turtle, a species found in the East, averages four inches (10 cm) in length and is the smallest of the turtles seen on these pages. The three-toed box turtle is more adapted to terrestrial life than most other American turtles. It ranges throughout the south-central U.S.*

*The "red-eared" turtle, which shares the box turtle's range, and is readily identified by the small but quite conspicuous red patches on the sides of its head, is extremely aquatic, taking to land only for nesting or rare overland migrations. The painted turtle is one of the most wide-ranging of the American turtles. Along the rim of its upper shell is a pattern of distinguishing red and yellow markings.*

**SPINY SOFT-SHELLED TURTLE**

**SPOTTED TURTLE**

**COMMON MUD TURTLE**

schools. A recent school of thought, however, suggests that the neck was more likely held rigidly out from the body. If so, it is difficult to see how a plesiosaur did its fishing. Jaws at the end of such an inflexible neck could hardly have been swung sideways fast enough to catch any but unwell fishes; and this makes it necessary to suppose that the whole body was maneuvered about in fishing. If so, the ungainly looking plesiosaur must have been a prodigiously athletic animal. Study of the limb girdles shows very broad surfaces for the attachment of powerful muscles for backing movements of the paddles, and perhaps the creature was indeed able to pivot its endless frame on a dime and snatch up astounded herring at the side. Personally, not being a paleontologist, I am going to remain skeptical about this notion that the plesiosaur's neck was stiff.

The turtles as a group are not truly aquatic, but are really amphibious reptiles. Their primary architectural specialty, the ancient and stubbornly cherished shell that they live in, is typically too heavy for a free-swimming existence. On the other hand, at the low-lying edges of the land where shallow water can be used to help buoy the armored body of a creature that spends its time creeping about the bottom, the shell is a successful device, and the majority of turtles has retained it since the earliest days of the Age of Reptiles. It has been tampered with only by turtles that have strayed from ancestral habits—by the tortoises that went farther ashore, and by a few kinds that have taken almost wholly to the water. In both cases the bony part of the shell has in one way or another been reduced.

THE most aquatic turtle of today is the huge leatherback, or trunkback *(Dermochelys)*, which reaches a weight of over 1,500 pounds (680 kg) and has shed the bony layer of the shell characteristic of all other turtles. Of the other sea turtles, the green turtle is by far the most highly adapted for swimming. Like the leatherback, it retains the swimming breast stroke even when crossing the beach to nest, while all the other sea turtles walk by moving the legs of each side alternately forward as most four-legged animals do.

Once a male sea turtle goes into the surf after hatching from a nest in the sand, it may never set foot on land again. In a few places in the world, however, green turtles of both sexes do come out on wild shores to bask. I recently visited one of these places—Pearl and Hermes Reef in the Leeward Islands of the Hawaiian archipelago—and saw green turtles and monk seals hauled peacefully out on shore together, flanked by rows of albatrosses. How extensive this

"RED-EARED" TURTLE

THREE-TOED BOX TURTLE

PAINTED TURTLE

## ALLIGATOR OR CROCODILE?

**ALLIGATOR**

*The best way to distinguish an alligator from a crocodile is to look at its head. The alligator has a broader, more rounded snout than the crocodile, and has upper teeth placed outside the line of teeth in its lower jaw. The fourth tooth on either side of its lower jaw is enlarged, but since they slip into a pit in the upper jaw, they are hidden when the mouth is shut.*

**CROCODILE**

*The crocodile's head tapers to more of a point than an alligator's, and its upper and lower teeth are pretty well lined up. It too has enlarged teeth on each side of the lower jaw. But they slant outward and fit in a groove outside the upper jaw. As a result, when the crocodile is viewed from the side they can be plainly seen even when the crocodile closes its mouth.*

basking habit used to be, before the depletion of the world's green-turtle populations, may never be known.

One of the important problems that aquatic animals face is finding their way about the trackless liquid masses of the oceans. A land animal lives surrounded by solid objects that keep their shape and positions and can be used as landmarks for travel guidance. But in the wastes of the water, landmarks are absent or very subtle, and it is hard for a land animal like man to figure out how an aquatic creature keeps from getting lost.

It seems fairly certain that none of the various kinds of marine reptiles simply wanders the oceans at random. The ichthyosaurs, for example, must have systematically cruised the seas on routes and schedules that let them rendezvous with schools of migrating fishes or kept them within the shifting temperature zones in which reptile metabolism goes on properly. If for no other reason, a seagoing reptile needs guideposts to be able to find the opposite sex at breeding time. It will never be known how the reptiles of the past accomplished these guidance feats, but something can be inferred from studying the migrations of fishes, seals, whales and the modern reptiles of the sea: sea snakes, a few crocodilians and above all the marine turtles.

THE fundamental aspect of sea-turtle ecology is that they live in the ocean and nest on land. Little is known about the relation between foraging territory and nesting locality in four of the five kinds of sea turtles. In one kind, however, the herbivorous green turtle, there seems to be a worldwide pattern of commuting between feeding territory and nesting beach. The two phases of the habitat rarely occur close together. Turtle grass grows in expansive stands only in protected water, while good nesting beach forms only where waves come in unhindered and break against the shore. This duality of habitat imposes on the green turtle the need to travel. In many cases the travel covers distances of hundreds of miles in the open sea, but the animals have adapted themselves to this situation to such a degree that they can hold a course through long periods of open-water cruising, and can home to a short section of breeding beach after a thousand-mile (1,609 km) cruise in the ocean.

The senses and signals used are not yet understood. About the only advance that has been made in studying them is the realization that the travel is clearly guided by a changing series of signs. The sense of smell is almost surely partly involved. Green turtles—and even more strikingly, ridleys—appear to test and retest the bottom, the washed beach and even the dry sand near the dune front by nosing it in a way that looks like smelling. The same sense may well tell cruising migrants of local changes in the water they swim through, and may allow them to follow smell gradients as homing salmon are thought to do. Little is known of the hearing sense in sea turtles. They make no regular audible sounds themselves, and so are probably not able to piece out their orienting technique by echo sounding of bottom contours, as some fishes evidently do. Incidentally, porpoises, along with their other arresting talents, have been found to squeak at fleeing fishes and determine their direction, range and even kind by appraising the echo that bounces back. The marked structural similarity of porpoises and the extinct ichthyosaurs suggests that the ichthyosaurs, too, may possibly have been echo-locaters; but the truth of this interesting idea will forever remain unknown.

When the known facts of the life history of the green turtle are carefully examined, the conclusion that it is able to navigate is inescapable. Navigation means either using dead reckoning or some kind of signposts. What the green turtle does seems too refined for any known biological mechanism to accomplish through dead reckoning. It may be that the animal steers by the sun and stars. A few years ago such talk sounded like moonshine. But then the great German zoologist Karl von Frisch discovered the sun-compass sense in bees, and in the following years celestial orientation was shown to guide birds and a long list of other animals, both vertebrate and invertebrate. In the case of sea turtles, it is not yet even known what they are able to see—whether their eyes see more of the night sky than ours, or less, or no stars at all. Even so, to suppose that they get guide signs from the heavens is no longer a bizarre and irresponsible whimsey, but the simplest and most logical theory to explain the facts.

Two important contributions made to the fauna of the waters by the archosaur stock, the ruling reptiles of Mesozoic times, were the phytosaurs and the crocodilians. Unlike the turtles, whose ecological background is unknown but which may never have gone through an interlude as completely land-adapted animals, the crocodilians and phytosaurs appear to have made the return to water after a long period of true terrestrial existence. Their ancestors very likely had acquired the two-legged gait later so widespread among dinosaurs and other ruling reptile stocks.

The phytosaurs and crocodiles are thus both secondarily aquatic and secondarily quadrupedal; and though there are important anatomical differences between the two, they looked alike and surely led similar lives. The phytosaurs were extinct by the Jurassic. The crocodilians live on, although much reduced in diversity. Most of their modern species are amphibious, but there were during the past confirmedly marine kinds, with paddle-feet, narrow jaws, reduced body armor and a high-finned swimming tail.

IN modern crocodilians all degrees of dedication to water life can be seen. A species of Central American caiman crawls far inland in fluctuating ditches, rills and wet meadows, where there is often insufficient water to cover its body. The alligator is more partial to deep water, and may enter the edges of the sea. Crocodiles have definitely entered salt water. One of them, the Asiatic estuarine crocodile, makes long ocean journeys and is known in coastal waters from eastern India and Ceylon to Malaya and Australia. The most inveterate fish eaters among modern crocodilians are the exceedingly slender-snouted Indian gavial *(Gavialis gangeticus)* and the false gavial *(Tomistoma schlegeli)*, which more than any other living crocodilian look like the phytosaurs of the Triassic. A difference between them and phytosaurs is the position of the nostrils: In gavials and other living crocodilians they are located at the tip of the snout, but in phytosaurs they were just in front of the eyes.

An important aquatic adjustment of crocodilians is the mechanism they have evolved for keeping water out of their breathing passages when feeding. The feeding process often involves committing mayhem upon intractable prey. The characteristic crocodile feeding technique is to seize a projection of its victim's body, spin on its long axis till the part is twisted off, then take hold again and repeat the grisly process till the prey is all used up. It is important to a crocodile to avoid drowning itself during such wild disorder. Accordingly, the nostrils are located on a pair of bumps at the end of the snout, where they can be thrust above the surface when the animal floats quietly on the water. Air entering them is conducted through two long passages which are separated from the mouth by a bony secondary palate. Just in front of the rear opening of these air tubes a muscular flap projects downward, and this can be pressed against another flap rising from the back of the tongue to make a valve that shuts the mouth off from the breathing passages. At the front end of the tubes the nostrils can also be tightly shut by muscles that work automatically whenever the creature dives. The crocodile is thus able to subdue, dismember and swallow its victims without getting water in its windpipe.

Like the crocodilians, the lizard group has lost its most thoroughly aquatic members. These were three lines of Cretaceous lizards of the group known as Platynota, mentioned earlier as having probably been involved in the ancestry of the snakes. Two of them, the aigialosaurs and the dolichosaurs, were small, long-tailed amphibious lizards whose limbs had in various degrees been converted to paddles. The aigialosaurs were the more primitive of the two and were evidently ancestral to the huge marine mosasaurs, probably connecting their line with that of the monitors. The mosasaurs were thus essentially giant seafaring monitors, with long, finned tails, paddle-like limbs with increased numbers of digital bones, and elongate, very toothy jaws. Most of them probably preyed on fishes and other reptiles, but some had heavy blunt teeth that seemed suitable for smashing the shells of mollusks.

Today the water reptiles, those that are committedly aquatic as well as those that are only partially so, live in every part of the water environment. Some are exclusively marine, some live in fresh water, some are confined to brackish water, and still others are able to pass casually between land and water or between fresh water and the sea.

A survey of the partly adapted modern water reptiles suggests some of the ways by which the rapprochement with water was probably originally made. Many newly marine reptiles of today have gone into the sea via fresh water. Those still partial to fresh water may live there semipermanently, or may enter water only to get food or to hide. Various lizards combine arboreal habits with aquatic interludes, like the tree iguana of the American tropics, which is nearly always found in trees over water, and the lizard *Lophura amboinensis* of the Malay and Philippine Islands. So do a great many kinds of snakes. This is what one would expect of creatures that have acquired their aquatic tendencies where forests are threaded by streams in which they can find refuge or food.

THE seeming paradox of the reptiles forsaking their hard-won place on land and sinking back into the sea—which is really no paradox at all—is heightened by the realization that one of the advantages drawing the animals back is one that helped bring them ashore to start with. The first stage of being either a land animal or a refugee in the water is to live in the shore zones, the swamps, marshes and tidal flats between water and land. At times these places are richer in food than either the land or the ocean. Even today you see the appeal of the fringe zones for terrestrial and aquatic creatures; they are drawn in from both environments for the sporadic and periodic harvests. Their presence in this in-between zone opens paths for natural selection in either direction.

One of the most important food resources offered by shores is their crustaceans. Lizards and snakes of many groups visit or inhabit salt beach or sea cliff for the wealth of crustacean food that may be concentrated there. A Javanese rear-fanged snake, *Fordonia*, has venom specially adapted for killing the crabs that the snake eats—so specialized that it is harmless to fishes and frogs. In Australia and the Sunda Islands several kinds of skinks catch crabs on rocky coasts. Among lizards the skinks are especially prone to venture into seaside habitats, especially in the Indo-Pacific—on Sunda Island one skink even chases fishes in the salt water of mangrove swamps.

Of the lizard-snake group, the most aquatic modern representatives are the cobra-like sea snakes of the Indo-Pacific. All the species of sea snakes are marine except one, which occurs in a fresh-water lake on Luzon in the Philippines. These snakes have nothing to do with the sea serpents of fable, nor even with the origin and evolution of the sea-serpent idea. The legends more likely grew out of inadequate observations of oarfish, giant squids or other sea monsters seen piece-meal among the waves by impressionable medieval eyes. The real sea snakes are not over nine feet (2.7 m) long—most are smaller. They have flattened tails and a compressed body. In most of the species the belly scales are not laterally broadened as in ordinary snakes, but are the same all around the body. Sea snakes thus lack one of the important adjuncts to terrestrial serpentine locomo-tion, and when they are placed on land they can only squirm and flounder about in a pitiable way. The nostrils are placed on the upper surface of the snout and can be closed by valves. The left lung is reduced, and the right one is greatly elongated, in some cases reaching as far back as the anus. Besides its function in respiration, this long lung is believed to serve as a hydrostatic organ—an inter-esting parallel with the development of the swim bladder of the bony fishes, which also is derived from a sac originally used by its ancestors as a sort of lung.

SEA snakes eat fishes, principally eels. Some of the fishes they swallow have spines, and instead of digesting or voiding these by natural channels the sea snakes get rid of them by pushing them out through the body wall. This sounds like a dismally unpleasant habit to me. Fresh-water snakes do the same thing occasionally, but evidently only by accident. I have personally seen two water snakes that had been killed when the still-attached spines of a swallowed fish had stuck through the wall of the body.

Sea snakes are as thoroughly aquatic as the leatherback turtle, but in one im-portant way they go beyond the leatherback in adaptation to the water environ-ment. About three quarters of the species are not bound to go back ashore to reproduce, but stay in the sea and give birth to their young alive. In the chapter on reproduction it will be shown that the switch from egg-laying to live-bearing is not quite so earth-shaking an evolutionary event as it might seem. It can be ac-complished in various makeshift ways. It has happened repeatedly in many kinds of animals that lead lives in which eggs are at a disadvantage in the environment of the adult. So the wonder is not so much that three quarters of the species of sea snakes bear living young, but that the leatherback, which has been in the water since the Cretaceous at least and possibly from as far back as the Triassic, should still cling to the awkward and hazardous nesting trips to the alien land.

Although the poison of sea snakes is specifically adapted to subduing the fishes it eats, it is also virulently poisonous to warm-blooded animals. Their venom is reckoned stronger than that of any other kind of snake, except possibly the tiger snake of Australia. Sea snakes, however, are generally timid and easygoing. Although there are scattered records of attacks, the snakes are handled with indifference wherever they are commonly caught in nets, either accidentally or to supply the Asiatic markets.

There are about 50 different kinds of sea snakes found throughout the tropical Indian and Pacific Oceans. One species, the common black-and-yellow sea snake *(Pelamis platurus)*, is pelagic, feeding on fishes in the surface regions of the sea. It wanders as far from the central sea-snake range as the east coast of Africa and the Pacific coast of the Americas.

After wanting for decades to catch a sea snake, I finally came upon three of them one day while looking for ridley sea turtles off the Pacific coast of Mexico in Sinaloa. The snakes were lolling idly at the surface as if sleeping in the sun, and I decided to try to catch them.

They looked absent-minded and easy to catch, but when I swept mightily with a long-handled dip net, each in turn darted straight down and, one by one, I lost them all. Then only last month my son Steven met a man carrying a live sea snake on a beach on the Pacific coast of Costa Rica. The man was going to use it for bait. Steven was tempted to buy it and bring it home but thought it might irritate officials along the way. The man let him hold the snake, however, and Steven tells me it felt soft-skinned and rubbery and not at all the way snakes generally feel.

The water snakes of the subfamily Homalopsinae include about 10 genera, some of which are wholly aquatic. They range from India and China to Australia and the Philippines and are found in both fresh and salt water. They eat fishes and are able to swallow their food when they are submerged. Their nostrils are crescent-shaped, and like the sea snakes they have valves that shut when they go under water.

Among modern snakes there is a continuous spectrum of adaptations between terrestrial and aquatic extremes. The water snakes of the genus *Natrix* usually use the water for feeding and concealment, but spend much of their time basking on the branches of overhanging trees or bushes. Some snakes, such as the black swamp snake *(Seminatrix)* and striped swamp snake *(Liodytes)*, emerge from the water only rarely. In the water they do little swimming, however, but instead crawl about among masses of floating water plants, foraging for crayfish and other little water animals.

AMONG lizards the most striking aquatic representatives of modern times are the big, gregarious marine iguanas that eat algae on cliffs on the Galápagos Islands. Perhaps just as confirmedly aquatic, if not even more so, is the South American caiman lizard *(Dracaena guianensis)*, which lives in tidal marshes of the Guianas and the lower Amazon. It eats snails and mussels, the shells of which it crushes with flat-topped teeth. A relative in northeastern South America is the brown water lizard, *Neusticurus rudis*, an expert swimmer that catches fishes, tadpoles and aquatic insects in forest-bordered streams. Nilotic monitors, some of which grow to a length of nearly seven feet (2.1 m), dive from the banks of East African rivers and seem almost as aquatic as the crocodiles that often slide in with them.

So, the reptiles no sooner got the hang of things on land than they went back to the maternal sea again. They did not go back as fishes or amphibians, but as reptiles. They returned to the ancestral medium with reptilian lungs and scales, still producing shelled eggs that had to be laid on shore. Their return to water was not a degeneration, any more than snakes' losing their legs was degeneration. It was a positive and profitable adaptation of plastic new stocks to an old environment. The environment they returned to was the primordial cradle of life, but it offers opportunity to advanced forms of life as well. It still holds strong attraction for all beings built of protoplasm, no matter what their commitments to the dry parts of earth may be.

BABY GREEN TURTLES, SHOWN SLEEPING ON THE WATER, THOUGH HATCHED ASHORE WILL SPEND ALMOST THEIR ENTIRE LIFETIME IN THE SEA

# The Aquatic Reptiles

After freeing themselves of a dependence on water by evolving a shelled egg that could be deposited on land, many primitive reptiles did an about-face and splashed back in. All major groups of modern reptiles, with the exception of the tuatara, now have their amphibious or completely aquatic species. Among these are snakes so specialized for life in the seas that they never venture ashore.

AN AMERICAN ALLIGATOR SHOVES OFF FROM A RESTING PLACE ON A RIVER BED. USING A SWIMMING METHOD OF ALL THE CROCODILIANS, IT

## The Many Attractions of Water

Different reptiles utilize the water for different purposes. The amphibious crocodilians use it to swim and hunt in. They also use it to cool off, for though found in warm climates they cannot tolerate great heat since they have little control over their own temperatures. If exposed for a long time to the hot-

test rays of the sun without water for a dip close by, a crocodile will die. Not unexpectedly the strong crocodilians are proficient swimmers, employing either the high-speed method shown above or a slow paddle. The only modern marine lizard is a species from South America's Galápagos Islands. It lives

THE SIAMESE SWAMP SNAKE HAS A GREEN CARPET OF ALGAE OVER ITS BODY, MAKING IT INVISIBLE TO THE SMALL FISHES THAT IT EATS

TUCKS ITS LEGS AND WEBBED FEET AGAINST ITS SIDES AND SURGES FORWARD WITH UNDULATIONS OF ITS POWERFULLY MUSCLED TAIL

along the shores and enters the water to feed on marine algae, rarely venturing out into swift currents. It has evolved a powerful flattened tail for swimming, and strong clawed legs for climbing back up on the volcanic cliffs that are its base of operations. Among the most aquatic of the reptiles are the big sea turtles; some species are able to swim as fast as a man can run the 100-yard (91-m) dash. Most sea snakes live their entire lives in salt water, feeding on fishes. The Siamese swamp snake at left spends a lifetime in fresh water unless dragged out of it, at which point it stiffens up like a board.

THE MARINE IGUANAS OF THE GALÁPAGOS ISLANDS ARE SKILLFUL SWIMMERS AND DIVE INTO WATER AT LOW TIDE TO EAT SEAWEED

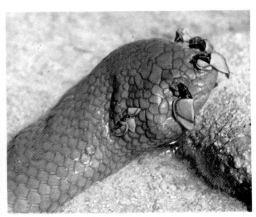

GOOSE BARNACLES growing on the head of a sea snake are a potential hazard, sometimes covering an eye, as here. The snake sheds them with its skin.

# Submersible Snakes

Most snakes can swim, but none are better equipped for it than the poisonous sea snakes with their paddle-like tails and laterally compressed bodies. They inhabit the warm waters of the eastern and western Pacific and the Persian Gulf, and are often seen swimming a thousand miles (1,609 km) from shore. Some even swim backwards. A factor enabling many of them to lead a completely aquatic life is their habit of giving birth to living young, thus freeing them of the necessity of ever leaving the water to deposit eggs on shore as the sea turtles must do. Most have dispensed with the enlarged abdominal plates used by land snakes in locomotion. Although all sea snakes must surface to breathe, they can stay submerged for long periods—apparently by extracting the oxygen they need directly from the water.

A SEA SNAKE from southeast Asia shows the typical conformation of many of its kind—a heavy body, with a tiny head and flattened tail. In several species the body is four to six times broader than the head.

A RIVER SNAKE, the South American anaconda is an expert swimmer and prefers the water, but is also adept on land. It eats many aquatic animals; one 25 feet (7.6 m) long contained a six-foot (1.8-m) caiman.

**MOUTH AGAPE**, an alligator snapper, largest of North American fresh-water turtles, extends its wiggling lure—a wormlike outgrowth of the tongue—and waits for fishes to nibble at it. When thus employed, the whitish or light-gray lure pinkens. The algae covering the shell help disguise the head in murky water and may also inveigle prey into coming closer to the lure.

DARTING TOWARD THE BAIT, a fish enters the mouth of the alligator snapping turtle. Instantly *(below)* the jaws snap shut and manipulate the fish into a swallowing position. If the fish were larger, the turtle would first tear it apart with its clawed front feet. The alligator snapper probably forages mainly at night and saves the lure for occasional use during sunlit hours.

A STRETCHABLE NECK, ALMOST AS LONG AS ITS SPINE, ALLOWS A SUBMERGED MATAMATA TO DRAW AIR THROUGH SNORKEL-LIKE NOSTRILS

# The Matamata, the Weirdest Turtle

The river-dwelling matamata of northeastern South America looks like one of evolution's mistakes. But its most bizarre features are the ones that serve it best. A cautious, extremely slow-moving predator of small fishes, it lurks on the murky bottom, camouflaged by a mottled greenish-brown skin and a ridged shell festooned with algae. The ear flaps and tabs on the head and neck are movable and act as fish lures. The long neck serves to thrust the tube-like nose out of the water for air, and also as a means of approaching quarry while the body remains almost motionless. When danger threatens, the neck cannot be retracted into the shell in the manner of most other turtles, but is curled under the carapace.

LYING IN AMBUSH, a matamata halts its movements as an unwary knife fish, attracted by waving lappets of flesh fringing its arrow-shaped head, swims closer and closer to its ready mouth.

SUDDENLY OPENING ITS JAWS and expanding its neck, the matamata creates a vacuum that sweeps the fish into its mouth with the inrushing current. Later on, it will expel the water.

**THE FACE OF THE MATAMATA** suggests an advancing army tank. The nose extends forward over the broad, V-shaped mouth, as do the tiny eyes. The fleshy jaws, which open into a hoop, lack the horny edges of other turtles' mouths since the matamata does not chew its food. Walking behind the head and swiveling neck is the rest of the body, covered by a lumpy shell.

# 6

# The Miraculous
# Shelled Egg

Reptiles are sexual animals and are the group that introduced internal fertilization to the vertebrate line. Thus, in a manner of speaking, they laid the foundation for the family unit in higher vertebrates, and from this came human society itself, with all its excitement and troubles. The ancestral amphibians deposited their eggs virtually naked in the water, and fertilized them by simply releasing sperm in the general vicinity. The hazards of such an informal operation to both sperm and egg are obvious. The reptilian egg, however, enters the world already fertilized, and packaged against environmental adversity. One need only compare the dozen or so eggs laid by the average lizard with the thousands laid by toads to see the economy the new method has brought.

But even an egg with a shell is delicate. It can incubate successfully only within a narrow range of conditions of temperature, humidity and concealment. It is thus not surprising to find that a few reptiles have independently hit upon the recourse that we think of as one of the main attributes of the mammals—that of producing living young.

All the live-bearing reptiles of modern times are lizards and snakes. Turtles and crocodilians produce only eggs, and so does the tuatara. It is significant that of the three reptiles which venture farthest north, even across the Arctic Circle, two—the European viper and the lizard *Lacerta vivipara*—bear their young alive. So does the slowworm *(Anguis)*, another venturer into northern regions. The cold ground of those areas, no doubt, is not well suited to incubating eggs. Neither is water, so far as shelled eggs are concerned, which explains why most reptiles with strongly aquatic habits also bear their young alive.

Many of the live-bearing reptiles, however, belong to groups that have egg-laying members too. The skinks, the lacertas, the boids and the vipers are examples. There are even species that lay eggs in some parts of their ranges but bear live young in other parts. This suggests that their viviparity—as the ability to produce live young is called—is not so formal an undertaking as it is in mammals, and this is true. Some reptiles merely keep the eggs inside the body for varying periods up to and after hatching time. In others there are extensive, placenta-like connections with the tissues of the maternal oviduct. In one type the yolk sac is merely plastered against the wall of the oviduct, and is used primarily for respiration. In a more advanced type the embryonic membranes, the chorion and allantois, interfold with maternal tissues and the embryo not only gets water and nourishment as well as oxygen, but conveniently has its excretory wastes taken away too. None of the live-bearing reptiles has dispensed with a big store of yolk that it carries as the main source of nourishment for the growing reptilian embryo.

ALL reptiles practice internal fertilization. In all modern forms except the tuatara the male has an organ kept turned outside in, in the base of the tail, and everted through the opening of the cloaca during erection. In the tuatara the transfer of sperm is accomplished by bringing the genital openings into contact, as in birds. This was probably the method used by the ancestral reptiles—it is clear, in any case, that the penis had separate origin in turtles, crocodilians and mammals on the one hand, and in lizards and snakes on the other.

Thus, male lizards and snakes have not just one, but a pair of hollow structures called hemipenes, which make up their copulatory organs. Located as they are in the tail just behind the opening of the cloaca, the hemipenes often give the tail of the male a thicker, more gradually tapering contour than that of the female, and in many species the sexes can be distinguished by this difference. A groove that serves as a channel for the sperm extends from the opening of the sperm ducts along the inner wall (which is the outer wall during erection) of each hemipenis, and the surface may be pleated or set with spines that keep it in place in the oviduct of the female during mating. Either one of the hemipenes may be used, but only one, the one nearest to the female, is everted and protruded from the cloaca during erection, which is brought about by a combination of muscular action and distension of the walls with blood.

Among different reptiles fertilization is scheduled differently with respect to the time of nesting. In most species it seems to occur, as might be expected, just before the eggs are laid; but in some the sperm may live on in the reproductive tract of the female and continue to fertilize eggs months or even years after copulation has taken place. The longest known periods of such deferment of fertilization are four years for the diamondback terrapin of the southern United States, and five years in the case of the tropical American cat-eye snake. The green turtle, which evidently mates only in the sea off the nesting beach, often does so *after* the female has gone ashore and laid her eggs. Since a given female makes her migration to the nesting ground only once in three, or more

## ADAPTABLE LIZARDS

*Although lizards do not fare well in cold climates, the Common Lizard of Europe has a wide range, and has become adapted to life in northern latitudes by bearing its litter of young alive (above), keeping the developing eggs as warm as possible by incubating them inside its body. In warmer regions farther south, however, females of the same species (below) produce their young by laying eggs to hatch.*

rarely two, years, it seems probable that sperm must regularly be stored for that length of time between nesting journeys.

In at least two races of lizards there appear to be no males at all, and young are evidently produced from unfertilized eggs. Such reproduction is known as parthenogenesis, or virgin birth. The most familiar case of parthenogenesis is that of the honeybee. The queen lays two kinds of eggs, some fertilized, some unfertilized. The unfertilized eggs produce the males, or drones; the fertilized eggs produce the workers. Ants, wasps and various other invertebrate animals sporadically or periodically reproduce by parthenogenesis. In some cases the parthenogenetic stage occurs at a time when conditions in the environment would make it difficult for the two sexes to meet for mating. How the two lizards evolved the practice, and why, is not clear. In some other species of lizards the females greatly outnumber the males and it is possible that this same phenomenon of parthenogenesis may normally alternate with bisexual reproduction among these lizard species.

Because the genitalia of male reptiles are internal, it is not always easy to tell the sexes apart. It takes a real expert, for instance, to determine the sex of a snapping turtle or alligator. However, in most species there are certain external features by which it is possible to distinguish the sexes of fully mature individuals. The two most obvious ones are size and coloration. There is no set rule about which sex may be the larger, but in many species it is the male that is bigger than the female. Where difference in color patterns exists, it is generally the male which has the more vivid coloration, as is usual in birds; but here again the situation is sometimes reversed. In some species the sexual coloration is a sort of nuptial dress, assumed for breeding and later abandoned.

Internal fertilization is a cooperative process, and to bring it about the sexes must find each other, and must be physiologically prepared for mating. Most if not all reptiles show some sort of courtship behavior by which the sex of a potential partner is determined, the coyness of the female is overcome, and a readiness to mate is generated in both members of the pair. Courtship often duplicates or blends with the expressions of rivalry and home defense between males, and since this whole complex of innate behavior is a hereditary part of the makeup of a species, it affords an interesting field for study.

THE courtship of a number of different snakes and lizards is a case in point. Although there are clear similarities in behavior patterns among the two groups, it has been found that most lizards recognize the female visually, while snakes depend on odor, trailing the female with their noses as well as with the tongue and Jacobson's organ. Male lizards put on quite a display among themselves—showing colored throat fans, erecting crests, arching their necks and affecting various gaits—but how much of this actually carries over into courtship is not surely known. Some of it, however, is brought to bear by the male on a prospective partner. When the female is thoroughly recognized as a female and her reticence overcome, the male lizard (like the males of some snakes) seizes her with his jaws, bends the base of his tail downward to maneuver the cloacal openings into contact, and insertion of one of the hemipenes is effected.

Turtles, both aquatic terrapins and land tortoises, carry out varyingly elaborate courtships which may include butting and nipping of the female by the male, or his swimming backward in front of her, fluttering his claws beside her face, or stroking her cheeks with his elongate fingernails. Among some species of pond turtles and among sea turtles, courtship is accompanied by competitive behavior among males. Two males, on rare occasions even three, may attempt to court the same female simultaneously and combine this with a mild struggle among themselves. In the pond in front of my house, during the mating season of the pond cooters, turtle heads are regularly seen in threes or fours. Off and on, for as long as two or three days at a time I have watched groups of these heads with a spotting scope, and while I could see little of what the bearers of the heads were actually doing, it did not seem to involve any very violent strife. The three heads simply stayed together in a restricted patch of water for a day or more at a time, and there were occasional outbreaks of splashing and finally the back of one of the turtles would come out of the water, indicating that mating was taking place.

A similar thing occurs among the green turtles at their nesting ground on the coast of Costa Rica. Here, too, the observations made have been only in snatches, and whatever subtleties of courtship behavior are carried out have not been seen. But during the early part of the nesting season the turtles mate out in front of the beach a few hundred meters beyond the surf line. For the first week or so of the mating time there are large numbers of courtship groups involving two males and one female. Among sea turtles, mating is a strenuous process. Attempts of the male to mount the back of the female involve a great deal of thrashing and splashing of water. Once the male attains the position on the upper shell of the female, however, he remains firmly anchored by two huge claws on his front flippers which grip the fore edges of her shell, and by a strong horn at the tip of his tail which curls up under the back edge of her shell. The only time male turtles are seen on shore at the nesting ground is when a copulating pair is caught by a breaker and thrown onto the beach right in the midst of their mating effort.

The courtship of the alligator is noisy and exciting. The bull bellows and exudes musk from glands on the throat and at the sides of the cloaca. When the female approaches, the two of them race about in wild circles, making a big wake that rocks the reeds and sends the fishes flying. The frogs stop singing and the waterfowl scream.

Closely related to courtship is rivalry and combative behavior among males. This sort of strife is not generally disorderly and injurious, but actually may serve a variety of useful purposes. It keeps the race physically on its toes, as it were, weeding out the weaker individuals as breeders. It brings about a distribution of territory, and thus lends order to both the reproductive process and the daily life of the individual. It establishes hierarchies of dominance and submission, and these again contribute harmony by forestalling more harmful untrammeled fighting. And just as courtship does, the fighting may help instigate glandular cycles involved in the mating process.

IN some species a by-product of fighting between males is to augment their often fuzzy capacity to recognize the female at mating time. Experiments show that when breeding males of certain lizards approach another of their kind, their mode of sex recognition is not, as one would expect, to search for signs of femininity. Instead, the criteria seem wholly negative: If the challenged lizard fights back it is a male; if not, the only alternative is to regard it as a female lizard and make appropriate overtures.

In many cases the contests between males are carried out without physical contact. The same ends are accomplished by various kinds of signals, posturings, and flashings of color patches, such as the throat fans of some lizards. The lusty, magnificent bellow of the American alligator, though not thoroughly understood, is partly a sexual call, but is partly used also as a territorial challenge.

A pattern of ritualistic sexual behavior quite as elaborate as that of some birds is the "combat" dance of some male snakes. The distribution of this extraordinary habit among the various snakes of the world is not accurately known, but it is found in a variety of species and genera—in snakes as unrelated as the rat snakes and the vipers, for instance. The exact aim of the dance is not known either. It may be prenuptial rivalry, or it could be a ceremonial way of contesting territory. I first saw this dance performed by a pair of cottonmouth moccasins years ago, and it still ranks as one of the most elaborate and stylized animal ceremonies that I have ever witnessed. It can best be compared to some of the most advanced ballets of birds.

It happened in 1941. My wife and I came upon the snakes in an open pool at the edge of a marshy lake in Florida. We were at once struck with the realization that something untoward was going on, and so sat quietly, watched raptly, and soon began taking notes and making sketches of the figures of the dance.

Throughout we were laboring under the mistaken impression that it was courtship we were witnessing, and because in a number of mated cottonmouth pairs that I had previously come upon the male was the smaller, I quickly decided that the smaller member of the dancing pair was the male in this case too. When the dance was over we took our notes and sketches home and wrote a little description that was later published in a zoological journal. In spite of our somewhat fundamental misapprehension regarding the sexes of the snakes, the description of the dance was faithful, and rereading it for the first time in 10 years brought it vividly back to mind.

WHEN first observed the snakes were gliding slowly about the pool, the forward third of their bodies raised high, crossed and interlocked in an open, symmetrical half-twist. The two heads, side by side, were bent downward at a slight angle to the necks, which were held almost vertical. The eyes stared out into space in a vacuous way suggestive of some sort of cataleptic seizure. Every few seconds the two snakes rapidly and in perfect synchronization smoothly recrossed their necks, reversing the relative positions of their bodies. Although there was little or no contact between the exposed portions of the bodies during this maneuver, the rhythmical precision of the reciprocal movements was such that it seemed as though two like parts of a single body were involved. From time to time the two would pause in their gliding traversal of the pool and in one place execute and reverse their figure eight several times before moving forward again with their odd dance.

After five minutes of such activity the smaller snake disengaged itself. Swimming slowly around the other two or three times, he inspected the raised forepart of his opponent's body minutely, touching it repeatedly with the tips of his tongue or with the end of his snout. Finally, he circled to the rear, looped himself across the partially submerged portion of the body of the other snake and shuffled and slipped himself slowly forward. On reaching the elevated thoracic region of the other, he threw a tight loop of his neck around it and began a spiraling climb upward. During this procedure the larger snake seemed intent on raising his head as high as possible above the water and, aided in this effort by supporting loops of the body of the other, he managed to reach a height of at least 17 inches (43 cm) for a brief time. When the lesser combatant had enfolded the other in two complete loops, and the heads of the pair were at nearly the same level, the rigid body of the big snake suddenly relaxed and yielded symmetrically to the enveloping coils of his opponent.

Thus intertwined, and with their heads posed almost vertically high above the surface of the water, the pair began what appeared to be a frantic and concerted effort to climb out of the water. At the same time the interlocked bodies swayed slowly back and forth, each swing being more extreme than the preceding. After 60 seconds of this, the combined upward struggling and rearing carried the snakes off balance and they fell over in a tangle of writhing coils.

This extraordinary operation was repeated three times, and in each instance, after the final collapse, both snakes would suddenly emerge to a third of their lengths, one two inches (5.1 cm) behind the other, with their snouts pointed upward. For from one to three minutes they would pose thus, all the while vibrating synchronously back and forth through an arc of about half an inch (1.3 cm). At this time the posterior two thirds of the bodies, which until now had been submerged and presumably intertwined, floated high in the water, side by side, motionless except for deep and rapid breathing.

After 45 minutes the big snake suddenly disengaged himself from the neck-loop of the other, circled the pool once and then struck out at top speed through the cattails in a series of zigzag rushes. For perhaps 30 seconds the snake left behind remained motionless in the center of the pool, watching the antics of his erstwhile partner. When one of the mad dashes of the swimming snake carried him to the edge of the open water, the one left in the pool appeared to realize the danger of losing contact permanently and set out in pursuit.

Then there was a wild chase through the emergent vegetation, far out into the open water and back to shore again, with the smaller snake apparently having no trouble following, at a distance of six to eight inches (15.2 to 20.3 cm), the erratic course taken by the larger one. After five minutes, however, the race ended abruptly when the big snake plunged through a dense sheaf of dead *Typha* leaves, crossed an open pool and concealed himself in a hassock.

This tactic seemed to baffle the other completely. He dashed about excitedly for a moment and then settled down to a deliberate and methodical search for the trail. Slowly he cruised a strip of some 50 yards (46 m) of the lake margin, quartering the zone of vegetation, and thrusting his snout into piles of trash and clumps of *Typha*. He vibrated his tongue continuously, flicking its tips against plant stems and floating sticks and into the water itself in a vain attempt to straighten out the intricate course.

We watched the fruitless search for some 30 minutes. Then the sun began to set and a cold rain started falling. When we left, the search was still going on.

Although the literature of that time had little to say about this most extraordinary of reptile rituals (and what there was mistakenly interpreted it, as we did, as courtship), similar behavior has now been observed both in the field and in reptile houses, in a number of species including rattlesnakes and colubrids. That a comparable set of complex stereotyped dance figures should have been clung to through all the time since rat snakes and rattlesnakes diverged seems extraordinary. That the same ceremony should have been carried over by the cottonmouth into the water is even more imposing evidence of genetic stability, or of utility, or of both. The comparative study of such behavior is the material of the field of natural history called ethology.

Practically all the eggs laid by reptiles are spherical or elliptical in shape. Those of snakes and lizards usually have flexible shells; those of crocodilians are hard-shelled, and the shells of turtle eggs may be either parchment-like or like glazed or unglazed porcelain. The eggs laid by a reptile at a given nesting may number from the two or three of the striped mud turtle (there is some indication that the African soft tortoise lays only a single egg) to the 150 or more of the hawksbill turtle. Some reptiles lay more than once during a nesting season. The usual number of nestings for the green turtle is three or four, but there may be as many as seven clutches laid, at intervals of nearly two weeks. The green turtle is one of a few reptiles of various kinds known not to nest every year.

In the big snakes, there appears to be an interesting correlation between the size of the individual and the number of eggs it may lay. On average, most snake species in the world lay between eight and 15 eggs at a time, but big constrictors will exceed this number. Among the African rock pythons, for example, a 14-foot (4.3-m) individual will lay about 20 eggs, but a 22-foot (6.7-m) snake produces up to 100. An 18-foot (5.5-m) reticulate python lays about 33 eggs, whereas a 25-foot (7.6-m) female is known to lay as many as 103 at a time.

Reptiles usually lay their eggs in sand, soil, humus or rotting logs. The nests range from an angle between tree roots or a scratch in the soil to the deep, cleanly urn-shaped cavity made by some female turtles or the mounded nest of the mother alligator.

Crocodilians diverge in nesting habits, largely because of the variety in their habitats. They all lay their eggs on land, but some simply bury the eggs, while others, like the American alligator, erect large structures from organic compost to serve as nests. These "mound-nesters," who generally live in swampy areas, search out a place at the edge of the water where moist debris—leaf mold, twigs, branches and even growing shrubbery—is available. This they scrape into a high mound, and then dig a cavity in the top of the heap, deposit the eggs in it, and cover it with material from the edges of the mound. Other species, such as the American crocodile, are "hole-nesters." They dig holes in the sand, as sea turtles do, usually in the sandbars and beaches of large rivers and lakes. Some scientists believe that the mound-nesters display more sophisticated evolutionary behavior than the hole-nesters, since the mounded nest raises the eggs above the waterlogged floor of the swamp, and the decomposition of organic material furnishes heat for incubation in a way a shaded nesting place cannot. Other scientists dispute this evolutionary superiority, maintaining that each crocodilian simply uses the nest type best suited to its particular environment.

O̲N a recent visit to the Caribbean coast between Honduras and Guatemala, I was stimulated to see on one clean stretch of salt beach the remains of nests and eggshells of three different reptiles all mixed together along the shore. One was the hawksbill sea turtle, which is fairly common in the waters of the region. The other was the American crocodile. The third was the big tree iguana, which has become thoroughly adjusted to a life that takes advantages from both arboreal and aquatic habitats. The mature iguanas spend nearly all their foraging and sleeping hours in trees overhanging the water. But if you seem to an iguana to be pressing it closely in its tree, it will simply let go and fall cleanly into the water. Under water it swims almost as well as a crocodilian, and conceals itself among roots or in cavities in the bank till the alarm is over. Different as the lives of iguanas, sea turtles and crocodiles are, the sand of the ocean beach offers the same attractions to all three animals as a place for incubating eggs.

With the end of the incubation period, the reptilian egg that has afforded such protection to the developing embryo becomes a prison to the creature

## A MATERNAL ALLIGATOR

*The female American alligator builds her nest by biting off huge mouthfuls of damp vegetable trash and combining them with mud to form a mound which may be six feet (1.8 m) wide at its base and a yard (91 cm) high. From 15 to 80 eggs are then laid in a hole scooped out of the top. This is promptly covered by material pulled from the rim and packed down smooth.*

*Unlike most reptiles, which abandon their eggs after laying, the alligator hovers about to guard the eggs from other animals. When it is time to hatch, the baby alligators make faint squeaking sounds, signaling their mother to amble over and help them tear open the mound.*

inside, and clearly some device is needed to enable the tiny hatchling to break out of the tough shell and membrane into the world. This is provided in snakes and lizards in the form of the egg tooth, a true if tiny tooth carried on the premaxillary bone and used by the little reptile to cut its way free. In turtles and crocodilians a similar function is carried out by the caruncle, a horny projection on the tip of the snout. Egg teeth and caruncles are shed soon after hatching—in the lizards and snakes usually within a day or two, in some turtles and crocodilians in two to four weeks.

Breaking out of the egg is a process that may take considerable time, even with the help of an egg tooth and certain secretions which, as hatching approaches, help the reptile young to free themselves by weakening the membranes and shells. In most reptiles, it takes several hours; in some, like the larger snakes, it may take as long as several days. Some of the turtles that spend their first winter after hatching in the nest may remain in the broken shell until the following spring.

Care for the eggs during incubation, or for the young after hatching, is not characteristic of reptiles. No turtle, for instance, shows any suggestion of brooding or parental care whatever. But a very few species do show various, in some cases surprising, degrees of instinctive concern for their young. One of the pythons, for instance, appears to brood its eggs, contributing perhaps some degree of metabolic heat to them—in any case, it coils around them in a protective fashion and will even continue to coil around the empty space if the eggs are removed. Certain colubrine snakes also have the brooding habit, as does one of the viper species. Among the lizards, the so-called glass snake and some related species coil around the clutch of eggs in the same way. Some of the American skinks of the genus *Eumeces* actively tend their eggs from the time they are laid in the nest until they hatch. During incubation, these lizards will ward off intruders, turn the eggs regularly and provide brooding warmth from their own sun-warmed bodies. One species even nursemaids its brood after the hatching: It assists the young to break out of the egg, sees to it that they can feed undisturbed, and cleanses their cloacal regions with its tongue.

Most crocodilians, as well, exhibit some degree of concern for their progeny. The alligator may return often to the nest site to fuss about, reshaping and moistening it during incubation and, when the croaking of hatched young is heard inside, to help them get out of the nest mound. After the young hatch, too, the mother may retain some of her solicitude for them. Old alligators are often found in the company of bands of small ones. This may in part be simply because the hatchlings proceed directly to the nearest open water around, as likely as not a "gator hole"—a deep pool sloshed out by a big alligator as a lurking place. Nests are frequently made near such holes, or the pools are made near the nesting site where the female keeps her watch during the incubation period. In the swamps and marshes in which alligators usually nest, a gator hole near the nest would be a logical place for the young to go to when they hatch—irrespective of whether they might get any protective attention from the parent. The point is debated by alligator hunters and other experts, but my own experience leads me to think that a gator hole with mother and hatchlings in it is indeed a rude sort of nursery. Certainly a female alligator in such a place surrounded by offspring that might be as much as several weeks old, can be expected to be much more irritable and resentful of intrusion than Florida alligators are at any other stage of their careers. I have twice blundered into such company while wading after frogs. Both times I nearly drowned myself in fright when the old alligator suddenly rushed halfway across the hole toward me in what seemed clearly a belligerent way. While in both cases the alligators stopped too short for biting, the point is that both mothers made overt defensive moves that quickly took my mind off any plan of putting their offspring in a bag, and would probably have had a comparable effect on any potential natural enemy. A few alligator men with whom I have discussed these incidents have assured me that the alligators that rushed at me were as scared as I was and were really only dashing away in panic. Other men who appear just as versed in gator lore say this is not so, that the seeming pugnacity is as real as I felt that it was.

In any case there can be no doubt that bands of sibling alligators hold together for long periods after hatching, and that their croakings draw the mother to them. That alligators can be called out into view by a man croaking like a little one is proof of this, and I saw other evidence of it only recently when my boys found a school of young alligators with an old one in a sinkhole at the edge of a lake, and called me to look at them. These were not new hatchlings but were at least two months old. Nevertheless, they were still banded together in a loose sort of way, and when found were for some reason croaking so loudly in ragged unison that they could be heard from 50 yards (46 m) off in the woods. They sounded like an uncertain chorus of some unknown frog. When we moved onto the bank an old alligator cruised away into a patch of maiden cane. Clearly the young were hers, and clearly she still kept scraps of instinctive concern for them—she glided out of the grass and moved a few meters toward us each time the bobbing young resumed their croaking, and also each time we imitated it. There was no sign of fight in her, but her moves were not the usual flight to the far fastnesses of the lake—they were sallies in our direction. Later we caught four of the little alligators. They ranged in length from $14^1/_2$ to 16 inches (36.8 to 40.6 cm). This alligator's maternal drive had thus lasted at least two months and perhaps three. Later it may disappear completely, and she will eat as many of her offspring as she can catch.

ONE of the conspicuous features of reptilian behavior is the seasonal aggregating of some turtles at nesting sites. The life cycle of an aquatic reptile is in broad outline a reversal of that of the amphibian. Most frogs go back to water to lay their aquatic eggs. Most water reptiles go to the shore to lay theirs. In some cases any kind of shore may be suitable, and the females thus are likely to emerge singly. But some turtles make long journeys to gather at a specially favored shore or in a few kilometers of preferred beach. The most massive known reproductive aggregations of any fresh-water reptile are those of a side-necked turtle, the arrau *(Podocnemis)* of the Orinoco and Amazon Rivers. Since the early naturalists explored the Amazon and Orinoco, the nesting assemblages of *Podocnemis* on certain sandy islands in the rivers has been a theme for excited reporting. The turtles come to the chosen islands from great distances up and down the river, and the gatherings are so vast that actual overcrowding of the nesting bars sometimes occurs. The adaptive function of the migration is not wholly clear. In part it may be dictated by the need for a special set of nesting conditions; but to some extent it may also be simply a hereditary tendency to cling to ancestral travel habits. In any case, the resulting aggregations are spectacular, and the people of the regions have, since pre-Columbian times, depended heavily on the nesting colonies for meat and eggs.

## THE WIDE-RANGING GREEN TURTLE

TORTUGUERO

*Although green turtles may wander 1,200 miles (1,931 km) from their nesting site to foraging grounds in the Caribbean, their travel routes remain in the realm of the unknown. The map above indicates their presumed paths, based on a tagging program initiated in 1955 at Tortuguero, Costa Rica, in which 3,000 adult female turtles were marked. Of these, 108 were later picked up at sites indicated by the turtles at the end of each row on the map. Those drawn between Tortuguero and the recovery sites show probable travel paths.*

All sea turtles appear to be migratory, and at least part of the periodic travel of all the species is back and forth between foraging places and nesting grounds. From information now available the hawksbill seems the least inclined to gather in groups for nesting, but even in that species some reproduction is weakly colonial and some carried out by widely spaced individuals.

The most clear-cut nesting migrations are those of the green turtle. Since this creature is herbivorous, most of its adult life is spent foraging on submarine pastures of marine plants. These may lie at considerable distance from the nesting beach. A favored nesting shore thus recruits turtles from different areas, and some of these may lie many hundreds of miles away. The green turtles of the coast of Brazil migrate 1,400 miles (2,253 km) to Ascension Island, a dot in the middle of the South Atlantic, battling contrary currents, and staying on course by signs and senses not yet understood.

PERHAPS the most dramatic of all marine reptile activities are the *arribadas*, or mass arrivals at an egg-laying site, of the ridley, the smallest of the sea turtles. There are two species of this round-shelled, big-headed creature: the olive ridley, which nests primarily in the Pacific, and Kemp's ridley, which frequents the beaches around Rancho Nuevo on central Mexico's Gulf Coast. Little was known about the nesting habits of this unremarkable-seeming turtle until an astounding reel of movie film, shot by a Mexican engineer in 1947 and then forgotten in a desk drawer for 13 years, was shown to a meeting of scientists in 1961. They watched spellbound as an apparently endless parade of turtles came slowly up an isolated beach to lay their eggs. Over a mile (1.6 km) of it was paved with ridley backs as some 40,000 Kemp's ridleys—probably the entire female adult population—came and went, each laying about 100 eggs and spending less than an hour ashore.

It is now known that these mass assemblages occur infrequently. Usually the females, who may nest twice during a season, come ashore in small groups. But when strong hurricane winds are blowing off the sea at nesting time, the females wait offshore for the winds to die down, and their numbers gradually build up into the immense throngs that surge ashore to lay their eggs. Sadly, *arribadas* of such staggering numbers as the one filmed in 1947 seem to be a thing of the past. By the mid 1970s, the world population of Kemp's ridley had been reduced to fewer than 4,000 partly through the depredations of coyotes that feast on unhatched eggs, and partly by the work of Gulf fishermen. In the decades after the mammoth 1947 procession, the largest reported *arribadas* each consisted of only some 2,000 females in spite of efforts to protect this most endangered of all sea turtles. Like turtles, some sea snakes periodically band together in the ocean, presumably for reproductive purposes. There is an old report of a migrating train of sea snakes 60 miles (97 km) long, and several species have been seen in smaller conclaves. Most sea snakes, however, bear their young live and do not form groups for nesting. The gatherings may be a means of mobilizing the sexes at mating time, but much remains to be learned of the social customs of sea snakes.

In fact, much remains to be learned about the whole subject of reptile reproduction. The great innovation reptiles made, putting a shell on their egg, seems a forthright, even simple evolutionary move. But the adjustments this single advance brought on have gone spreading and weaving through the lives of all of us for 300 million years. The songs of birds are because of the egg with a shell, and so are the thoughts of men.

BREAKING FROM ITS EGG, A 10-INCH (25.4-CM) BABY CROCODILE MAKES ITS ENTRY AT LONDON'S ZOO. GROWN IT MAY REACH 16 FEET (4.9 M)

# Courtship and Egg-Laying

As the first vertebrates to venture far from water into the continental heartlands, reptiles had to evolve hardy eggs and the advanced mating practices that go with life on land. The hardiness of their eggs is confirmed by the one above, which was laid in Africa but hatched in London. Some of the odd ceremonials connected with reptile reproduction are depicted on the following pages.

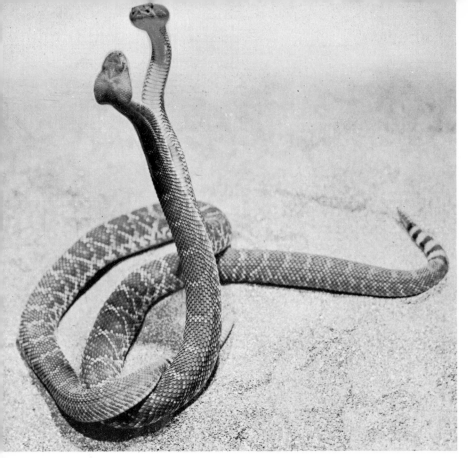

TEST BY WRESTLING between two red diamondback rattlers *(above)* starts out with one climbing up the other. When they overreach and collapse inconclusively *(below)*, they writhe and spar in preparation for the next fall.

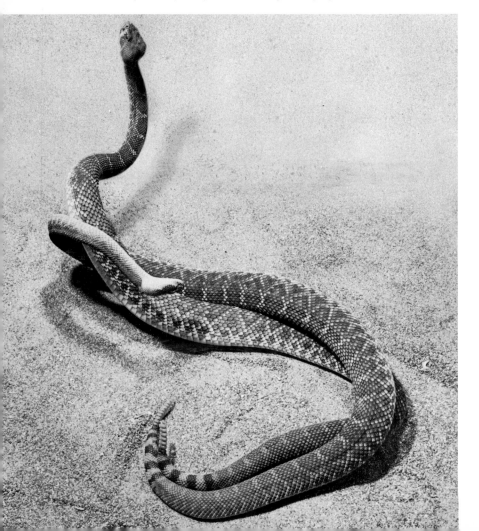

# Combat and Color among the Males

The generally accepted practice in the animal kingdom, when the time comes to reproduce the species, is for the males to put on a show that will impress and captivate the females—a courting activity which extends right up to man. As in other matters, however, reptiles have their own ways of doing things: Their efforts at courtship time, while still confined to the males, seem to be directed more at discouraging male rivals than at winning over females.

The show the males put on is impressive. Some may engage in ritualistic combat, like the two diamondback rattlers shown at left, wrestling gracefully and sinuously to repeated falls. Others, like the anole lizard opposite, put on gaudy colors and spread frightening fans to intimidate rivals. Some lizards dance, others affect strange, stiff-legged gaits. The net effect is to single out the fittest members of the male population as breeders, leaving the weaker to go elsewhere—a useful practice that may date back to earliest reptile times. As for the females, though they seem generally oblivious to these exaggerated male antics, they succumb in the end and mating takes place.

TEST BY INTIMIDATION is practiced by the male anole lizard, which can spread these flaccid folds beneath its chin to a fan of bright color at mating time. A cartilage rod inside serves to flare out the lavender skin.

THE FRUITS OF LABOR, three large eggs, lie beside an indigo snake as she lays a fourth one. Here photographed in captivity, she would normally lay her clutch in a burrow underground.

## The Mother and Her Eggs

The end product of reptilian mating represents one of the great triumphs of evolution: an egg that comes into the world fertilized and fortified, externally by a shell, internally with food and water for the entire development of the embryo inside it. Such an egg has a pretty good chance of surviving on its own, and indeed, there are few reptile eggs that get any maternal attention at all throughout the period of incubation. Turtles, who lay the most eggs—up

TWO LARGE WHITE EGGS OF A TEMPORARILY TAILLESS TURKISH GECKO SHINE THROUGH THE SKIN OF HER BELLY. SOON SHE WILL LAY to 400 a year in the case of sea turtles—care for them the least, generally abandoning them to the sand or earth in which they bury them. Crocodiles, lizards and snakes normally lay fewer eggs, but may do more for them—exploiting the sun to keep them warm, or supplementing sunlight with the warmth generated by decay in nests of rotting vegetation. Still others guard their eggs against predators, and one, the Indian python, broods them like a hen.

**THE BURIED NEST** of a peninsula cooter, a Florida fresh-water turtle, shows a clutch of eggs buried deeply, with two left at the sides, possibly as decoys to mislead nest-robbing predators.

THEM UNDER A STONE OR OTHER SHELTER, TO HATCH IN A FEW MONTHS AND GROW, LIKE THEIR MOTHER, INTO AMIABLE HOUSE PROWLERS

CHORION

SHELL

ALBUMEN

AMNIOT

YOLK SAC

**A**
(See detail opposite)

EMBRYO

UMBILICAL STALK

## HOW THE EMBRYO FEEDS

Food conduits in the form of blood vessels in the lining of the egg's yolk sac (circled area A, opposite) take up nutritious chemicals from the rich golden store of sugars, starches, fats and proteins laid away in the yolk. The blood proceeds to circulate them throughout the whole yolk wall. Thus they reach the abdominal region of the embryo where they are in turn used for growth. Waste chemicals pass out of the embryo into the fluid of the allantois.

## HOW THE EMBRYO BREATHES

Gas vents in the porous shell wall (circled area B, left) are revealed as small holes in the enlargement at right. These let life-giving oxygen into the alligator egg and poisonous carbon dioxide out of it. The oxygen is captured by oxygen-hungry hemoglobin molecules in the blood vessels of the chorion, which carry the vital gas by way of the allantois to the embryo. The carbon dioxide escapes from the blood by a process of seepage known as gaseous diffusion.

ALLANTOIS

B
(See detail at right)

# Inside the Egg

Compared to the simple eggs of fishes and amphibians, which are laid in water and often depend on it to bring fertilizing sperm to them, the reptile egg is a staggering innovation—the product of eons of development which started when the reptiles' amphibian ancestors first took up internal fertilization. The alligator egg at left, with its embryo in a halfway stage of development, typifies the complexity of most reptile eggs. The embryo in the center is connected by an umbilical stalk to the primary food supply, the yellow yolk sac, and is encased in the amniotic sac, an envelope filled with fluid which laves the embryo and cushions it from shock. The amniotic sac and yolk sac, in turn, are surrounded by still another envelope, the allantois, which in the early stages of development grows out from the embryo's hind-gut. The allantois gets larger as the embryo grows and the yolk shrinks. It serves both as a storage bladder for uric acid, ammonia and other wastes, and as a conveyor for incoming oxygen and outgoing carbon dioxide. Another membrane, the chorion, encloses allantois, amniotic sac, yolk sac and embryo in a tough, resilient envelope closely associated with the eggshell itself. In crocodilians and turtles, the chorion contains egg white, or albumen, which serves to supply the embryo with water and probably some food.

PICKING UP AN EGG, a female crocodile gently nudges her progeny into her fanged jaw to carry it from the nest to water. In the nest below ground, hatching young signal their readiness for air and water with a penetrating chorus of yelps. When she hears them, the mother will smash through even substantial man-made barriers in her haste to dig out her offspring.

## The Crocodile's Mother Love

Perhaps the most astonishing example of parental concern, rare among reptiles, is that of the Nile crocodile, which cares for her young with a tenderness belying her fearsome appearance. The female lays as many as 60 eggs in a nest away from the water's edge, then covers it with nearly a foot (30 cm) of soil. For three months she lies nearby, lunging at intruders and eating virtually nothing. When the young are ready to face the world, the female scrapes open the nest and gathers all its members, hatched and unhatched, into a capacious pouch in her mouth. Thus laden, she proceeds to the water, where she releases her offspring. They remain in the shallows for 12 weeks, their parents and other adults on hand to answer distress calls, before venturing out into the world on their own.

A NILE CROCODILE TRIES TO HATCH A TARDY EGG BY ROLLING IT ACROSS HER PALATE

A NEWBORN CROCODILE, its tail dangling into the shallow river water, prepares to leave the haven of the maternal mouth.

# Cutting Out to Meet the World

How tentative and experimental the reptiles still are in their efforts to abandon the egg and bear their young alive is dramatically demonstrated by a special little tool which all of them, even the live-born, still have. This is the egg tooth, a sharp protrusion on the snout with which a baby reptile can cut its way out of its tough, membrane-lined shell. To be sure, in live-bearing species which have no need for it the egg tooth is degenerating (even the egg-layers drop it soon after birth). But it still stands as a reminder of the difficult escape problem the shelled egg has always presented for the beakless reptiles.

CUTTING ITS WAY into the world, a baby scarlet snake makes the first slit in the egg's shell *(top picture)*. Several hours later, it has enlarged the hole sufficiently to crawl out, fully formed.

CLOSE-UP of the baby snake's head *(opposite)* at the moment of emergence from the shell shows the egg tooth as a tiny triangle at the top of the picture just left of where the mouth begins.

# 7

# Myths, Man and the Reptiles

Reptiles and people have always been important to each other. In the old
days the relation was the natural give-and-take of ecology. Today we
have taken the earth in hand, and in the lives of the reptiles we loom much
larger, while they count for less in ours. But in the interim our history
was forever marked by the presence of these cool, dry, silent creatures. Their
sign is still on the human spirit all over the world, in their pervasion of
mythology and religion.

In the Judeo-Christian tradition the snake is generally assigned an evil
role. The temptation of Adam was instigated by the serpent and led to Adam
and Eve's expulsion from the Garden of Eden. For his treachery the snake
was condemned to roam the earth forever on his belly, a despised and abased
being. The early Church looked upon descendants of the primeval tempter
with dislike, and the story goes that St. Patrick took his staff in hand in the
Fifth Century and permanently drove all these symbols of evil from his
beloved Ireland. Actually, the present snakelessness of Ireland is due to
pretty much the same factors that cause a lack of elephants there. In the 19th
Century—whether in the spirit of science or iconoclasm it is hard to say—

someone imported a shipment of snakes back into Ireland, in an effort to establish them there. The final outcome of the experiment is not reported, although the *Edinburgh New Philosophical Journal* for April 1835 remarked, "We have learned from good authority that a recent importation of snakes has been made into Ireland, and that at present they are multiplying rapidly within a few miles of St. Patrick's tomb."

MANY thousands of years before St. Patrick raised his staff, though, and many thousands of miles away, people of wisdom and religion cast the snake in a host of varying roles. The Polynesians also called him the seducer of the first woman, Hina; but unlike Eve, Hina later slew her tempter and buried his head in the sand. From the head soon grew a tall coconut palm, and imprinted on its fruit Hina recognized—as may her descendants even today—the eyes and mouth of the serpent who betrayed her. In Norse mythology the great Midgard Serpent was also a symbol of omnipresent evil; it was said to lie coiled in the sea, waiting for the time when it could sever the roots of the tree of life, Yggdrasil, and bring about the end of the world. The preclassical Greeks had a more positive attitude. They believed that Gaea, the earth mother, took the form of a serpent below ground and they kept a large snake in her temple to honor her. Similarly, among the American Hopi Indians the snake was a great life force residing deep in the earth. As such it came to symbolize man's primal, earthy nature, coiled in the lowest regions of the spine, with implications for both good and evil.

The Hopis still pay homage to the powers of the snake in their yearly Snake-Antelope ceremony, held every August on the Hopi reservation in Arizona. The ceremony celebrates the marriage of man's two governing centers—the spiritual, symbolized by the lofty horns of the antelope, and the physical, the mother earth from which all life springs, symbolized by the snake. The two-day ceremony culminates in the famous Hopi snake dance, in which 24 Snake Chiefs dance amid the crowds with rattlesnakes, bull snakes and gopher snakes they have gathered from the surrounding desert. One by one, to the beat of drums, each dancer selects a snake from a pot of writhing coils and places it in his mouth. Holding it gently between his teeth just below the head, he circles around the clearing. He then hands the snake to a member of the Antelope Clan, who sings to it soothingly as the dancer returns to the pot of snakes to get another one. Finally the celebrants carry the snakes back to the desert, bless them and dispatch them to carry to the ends of the earth the message of the renewal of all life.

The serpent god of the ancient Mexicans was of an even more exotic aspect. Combining the splendid plumage of the tropical trogon or quetzal, the most magnificent bird in the Americas, and the sinister features of the indigenous rattlesnake, he was Quetzalcoatl, the feathered serpent, the "fair god" of the Toltecs and Aztecs. The mighty quetzal came to symbolize the wind, and the irascible rattlesnake the whirlwind; put together they were the god who pushed the clouds. Pushing the clouds brought rain, and so put fertility into the land; from there all blessing flowed.

Like most primitive gods, Quetzalcoatl had such varied manifestations that it takes a specialist to trace them. One of his favorite pastimes was said to have been sailing around the Gulf of Mexico on a raft of serpents. When the Spaniards landed in Mexico, the emperor Montezuma at first thought they were Quetzalcoatl and his retinue coming home. This misapprehension delayed Indian resistance to the invasion, and that hastened the fall of the Aztec government. The feathered serpent was a prevalent motif in pre-Columbian architecture and decoration through most of southern Mexico, Yucatan and Guatemala.

The snake of mythology tended to be a pretty weird creature, laden with unearthly symbolism. He lent a touch of the supernatural to everything he associated with, guided man's existence in ways never quite understood. In Hindu legends he comforted the gods themselves. The supreme god of the Hindu pantheon, Vishnu, is said to sleep between incarnations on the coils of the noble cobra Shesha. Wound about the earth, the cobra allows his seven heads to rise over the god as shade for Vishnu's eon-long siesta. This is why Indians are kind to cobras. Shesha's descendants were the serpents called Nagas, a fabulous race whose members were sometimes said to exceed 400 miles (644 km) in length. The Nagas and their wives, the Naginas, guarded bodies of water, caused earthquakes and volcanic eruptions, ruled the annual monsoons, and scattered plague and famine liberally among humans. They were generally ornery, unpleasant creatures, but with the inconsistency typical of the old gods, they also took a benign interest in the conception and birth of human children—again a natural association of snakes with fertility. Today in India the Jogi tribes catch cobras and house them in little pots and baskets, to symbolize the human triumph over the Nagas' malevolence.

It was the custom in many cultures to propitiate the great serpent gods by small kindnesses to the snakes of the countryside. In Eastern Europe and the Middle East snakes were welcomed in farmhouses and allowed to live there almost as benevolent household gods. When the cry of the house adder was heard in the evening (needless to say no adder can cry, but that is quibbling), a saucer of milk, half covered by a clean white cloth, was put out and the adder would come and drink. At least, the milk would sometimes be gone in the morning; whether it disappeared in houses that had no dog or cat is not recorded. In Africa snakes nosing about the house were assumed to be reincarnations of dead relatives and were venerated. But the snake charmers who have dazzled visitors to the East for centuries did not laud the snakes so much as challenge them. They proved that a person could at least for a moment conjure up a magic as powerful as that of the immortal snakes.

T HE best snake charmers have always lived in the East. Some of the things they do are not yet wholly understood. Although through the centuries Indian snake charmers have been given a great deal of critical attention by spectators determined to be objective and "bring out the true facts," no really adequate appraisal of the art has been made. Some "charmed" snakes have in fact had their fangs drawn or their mouths sewn shut, but obviously such tactics are not the whole answer, because in most cases the snakes are unharmed and quite able to bite. In fact, a few years ago a snake charmer in Baltimore was bitten by one of her cobras and died. The snake charmers of India are said to have to swear a holy oath that they will keep a snake only six months, and so they must constantly renew their stock with wild specimens. If they fail to keep their promise, their masters warn, they will be bitten by one of the snakes whose liberties are being violated.

Herpetologist Clifford Pope thought that charmed snakes may just be lethargic from overeating, and compared the charmed snake to one basking in the sun, who will not be frightened away by talking or even shouting.

## MYTHICAL REPTILES

*Medieval men entertained some bizarre notions about reptiles. Draco the Dragon was described in a 12th Century bestiary as the biggest of all living things. The strength of this serpent-like beast was supposed to lie not in its teeth, but in a long coiled tail that could suffocate an elephant (above). Beyond these fancies, its genesis remains obscure, but the Crocodylus (below) clearly derives from the African crocodile. It was named for its "crocus" color. Bred in the Nile, it was correctly assumed to be active at night, to incubate its eggs in the earth, and to eat people. However, its long legs, clawed feet, prominent ears and tail are imaginary.*

Certainly, it is not the magician's wooden flute that charms the animal, or any other background noise. Pope recorded an experiment in which snakes were blindfolded and then subjected to terrific noises. Bugles were blown and large tin cans were beaten near their heads, but the snakes, being stone deaf, showed no reaction whatsoever. They did, however, react immediately when anyone walked or moved a chair nearby—they sensed the vibrations such movements transmitted through the ground.

However, the belief that music charms snakes dies hard. There is a story mentioned by Laurence M. Klauber, in his monumental work on rattlesnakes, of a berry picker who used a mouth organ to render rattlers harmless while he went about his work. Another very tall tale recalls an American Indian who trained a band of rattlesnakes to join him in a mixed chorus: The snakes, which ranged from small to large, carried the soprano, alto, tenor and bass parts with their rattles. Apart from the music, however, one thing all snake charmers, whether in India or among the Hopi Indians, have in common is incessant movements of their arms and bodies and, in snake dances, of their legs. It is possible that snakes may be bewildered by the rhythmic motions, or possibly even hypnotized in some way. In any case, a skilled snake charmer conjures up a mood of dreamlike horror in the small pageant of human, snake, flute and basket. Reported one traveler in Egypt for the *Pictorial Museum of Animated Nature*:

"I have seen at Cairo a man who came from above the Catacombs, where the pits of the mummy-birds are, who has taken a cerastes (a horned viper) with his naked hand from a number of others at the bottom of a tub, put it upon his bare head, and tied it about his neck like a necklace. After which it has been applied to a hen, and bit it, which has died in a few minutes: and to complete the experiment, the man has taken it by the neck, and beginning at the tail has eaten it as one would do a carrot or stock of celery, without any seeming repugnance."

PHYSICALLY less eerie than the snake, and in manner less menacing, the turtle has nonetheless played just as great a part in myth and legend. Just as the snake is a symbol of great mystery and magic, the turtle usually stands for great stability; even before Aesop made him the symbol of steadfastness and perseverance, he generally played a role of integrity and support. In legends from India to Japan to North America the earth was said to lie upon the back of a great turtle, who supported it amidst a cosmic void. In ancient China, Kwei, the divine tortoise, was the most benevolent of all the creatures that supervised the earth's creation. He himself gave birth to the great guardian turtles of China and Japan, one of whom bears the island of paradise on his back. According to Hindu legend, the universe is recreated every four billion years, when the supreme god Vishnu is reincarnated into a turtle. Suspending himself in space, he carries on his back the great churn with which the gods and demons stir the world to life again. They uproot Mount Meru and set it in the sea as a churn staff. They somehow persuade the great snake Vasuki to throw a half hitch of his body around the staff and let himself be used as a churn rope. The gods and demons churn for a thousand years, until finally a goblet of amrita, the liquor of immortality, and Lakshmi, the goddess of beauty, arise from the milky void and initiate the world once more. Once the creation is complete, Vishnu retires for his cosmic rest, but his turtle avatar remains the base of creation: On the turtle's back stands a great elephant, and on the elephant's back rests the world.

The stories of turtles who support the world extend even into modern mythology. According to one widely circulated but unsubstantiated anecdote, the philosopher William James, lecturing on the structure of the solar system, was interrupted by an elderly lady who claimed she had a theory far more sensible than his. "We don't live on a ball going around the sun," she said. "We live on a layer of earth on the back of a giant turtle." Not wishing to invite a scene, James decided to reason gently with her. "If your theory is correct, madam," he said, "what does this turtle stand on?" "That's a very good question," she replied, "but I can answer it. He stands on the back of another, far larger, turtle." James sighed. "Then what does the second turtle stand on?" The old woman grinned triumphantly. "You're a very smart man, Mr. James, but it's no use. It's turtles all the way down."

Not every culture looked upon the turtle as an invincible bulwark of human civilization. To the ancient Egyptians he was anathema, not to be used as any kind of medicine (unlike most of the rest of the natural world) or accorded the semidivine status of snakes and other reptiles. Turtles, rather, were creatures of watery darkness, the natural enemies of the supreme sun-god Ra. "May Ra live and may the turtle die," ran a common epithet. Similarly, Confucius cast some doubt on the reliability of the turtle when he pointed out that the tortoise carried a record of the Eight Virtues on its back only because otherwise it was unable to remember them all. The previously highly venerated turtle became, after Confucius' Fifth Century B.C. observation, something of a moral outcast.

Of all reptiles, crocodilians achieved perhaps the greatest mythical notoriety. They were the prototypes of the dragons, those fantastic creatures of claw and scale that haunted the dreams of innocents in every culture. The dragon of European romance was probably nothing more than an African traveler's recollection of the Nile crocodile, enlarged several times. Even in its native Egypt this great crocodile was accorded semidivine status, but with the usual ambiguity of ancient religions he was both revered and abhorred. The crocodilian god Sebek was the personification of evil, a creature of darkness who occasionally tried to swallow the sun and caused widespread panic until the eclipse passed and the sun was restored to the world. Sebek's priests inhabited a city called Crocodilopolis, where, according to the First Century B.C. Greek geographer Strabo, they spent their time catering to the jewel-bedecked crocodiles of the city's many shrines, feeding them milk and honey and, when they died, placing their carefully mummified bodies among the royal tombs. Stories of maidens sacrificed to sate the crocodile-dragons' hunger were fantasies in Europe but often all too real along the crocodile-infested waters of Africa. The practice of throwing virgins into the rising waters of the Nile every year to placate the crocodiles and ensure adequate fertilization of the surrounding land persisted until the Seventh Century, when Moslem conquerors requested the substitution of clay or wood dummies for real women. In this abbreviated form the practice has continued down to the present day.

The dragons that fill the legends of the Far East were probably based upon the Chinese alligator and the great salt-water crocodile that haunted China's southern coasts. Unlike Western dragons, Chinese dragons are cool, do not breathe fire and are usually serene. Originally a fertility figure, the dragon

## HOW TO HANDLE
## REPTILIAN PETS

*A small lizard can be held by pressing the thumb gently on a hind leg. Grabbing it by the tip of its tail may break it off.*

*Grasping a snake's neck carefully behind the head will keep it from biting. Squeezing too tightly will increase its struggles.*

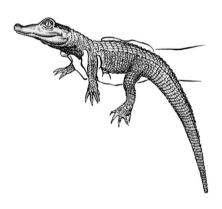

*Crocodilians may be held in the manner shown above. Reptiles should not be disturbed for an hour or two after eating.*

grew into a cosmic symbol for the benevolence of natural forces, and finally into the sovereign protector of Chinese culture. Eventually, the dragon came to symbolize the emperor himself. In Chinese legend dragons supported the sky and kept the earth's rivers on their courses; their disquiet manifested itself in thunderstorms, and their benevolence allowed the harvest to proceed.

All over the warm parts of the earth, crocodilians remain objects of veneration and worship. In many places the homage is a sort of bribery—the beasts are fed to keep them in a good mood. Other cults carefully distinguish between crocodiles that have attacked people and those that have not. At Lake Itasy in Madagascar a yearly proclamation is made announcing formally to the crocodiles that the evil ones among them—those that have killed someone during the past year—will be liquidated in their turn, and that all upright crocodiles should stay out of the way. When a swimmer is taken by crocodiles in the lake, a council of village elders assembles on the shore to request that the crocodiles hand over the culprit, and to assure the innocent ones that no ill will is felt toward them.

Both picturesque in appearance and heavily laden with allegorical associations, crocodilians have served many civilizations as heraldic symbols. The dragon has become a classic symbol for aggressive invincibility, appearing as a fierce emblem on shields and banners all around the world. The Manchu emperors used it, and so did the Mikado of Japan, and so did the British, who for a time used it in the royal arms when they incorporated Wales. The turtle, similarly, has decorated flags all through history as a symbol of steadfast invulnerability. In American heraldry, not surprisingly, it is the native rattlesnake that plays the major role. DONT TREAD ON ME was the warning motto of the coiled rattler pictured on the banner of John Proctor's Independent Battalion of Westmoreland County when these Pennsylvanians went to war against the British, and the first Navy Jack carried a rattler out onto the high seas, stretched diagonally from lower right to upper left across the 13 red and white stripes symbolizing the colonies. One of the original companies of the Marines also had a rattlesnake painted on its drum when that newly formed corps first saw action.

THE reptiles have had a peculiarly intimate influence on human life because all over the ancient world they were thought to have extraordinary medicinal properties—and in many places they still are. The Egyptians dosed blindness in humans, thought to be caused by Sebek's malevolence, with large quantities of crocodile potions, made primarily from dung and fat. According to the massive text on natural history that the Roman naturalist Pliny produced in the First Century A.D., extracting the fat about a crocodile's heart would, contrary to popular supposition, do nothing to enhance the success of a lawsuit. However, Pliny assured, crocodiles were quite potent healers of many other human miseries. Stones from a crocodile's stomach could prevent aching joints, crocodile teeth were aphrodisiacs, burned crocodile skin mixed with vinegar was as close to an anesthetic as the Romans could manage. Pliny's injunction to dose coughs with "dragon" meat and oil was obeyed even in North America in the 1880s, when tuberculosis patients would journey to the southern states to seek out alligator oil and rub their chests with it to cure their disease.

Snakes for some reason became trammeled with even more medicinal superstitions than crocodiles. Aesculapius, Apollo's son and physician to the

Olympian gods, was immortalized in the heavens as the constellation Serpentarius, the man holding a giant serpent. To this day, perhaps coincidentally, the symbol of the medical profession in America is the caduceus, the staff of the god Hermes, about which are entwined two snakes. Throughout Europe both viper broth and the boiled flesh, either prepared at home or bought at the apothecary's, were popular remedies until fairly recent times. Among the ancient Gauls the magic spread from the adder itself to a potent charm called *glein neidr*—serpent's egg, or adder stone. These adder stones were actually old beads found about the countryside, but the Druids claimed that they were produced by a group reproductive effort of a summer congress of adders, and held some of the magic of the parent snakes. Adder stones strengthened their owners in legal disputes, and helped them gain audiences with kings. In Celtic parts of the United Kingdom the beads were until very recently still valued by country people for driving away an ague or protecting children from such childhood ailments as whooping cough. In the same way, "snake oil" is still a potent panacea in many rural parts of the United States.

In modern times perhaps the greatest contact reptiles have had with man's daily life has been in their new role of pet. In the Western world, when a pet was taken into the bosom of a family it was until lately generally furred or feathered, and hardly ever a scaly reptile. Now, however, at first in Europe and a bit more slowly in the United States, reptiles are being welcomed into households as agreeable and rewarding animal companions. Not long ago, little turtles, anole chameleons and baby alligators were almost the only reptiles to be found for sale in American pet stores. Today, many shops offer a varied line of lizards, snakes and turtles, and the pet industry has suddenly become one of man's main ways of exploiting reptiles to his material gain.

Turtles are by far the most popular reptilian pets. Until the 1970s the small red-eared turtle, hatched for the trade by the millions in Mississippi Valley hatcheries, was a common fixture in many American children's rooms. Then the federal government discovered that these seemingly innocent pets were actually the cause of a sizeable percentage of the salmonellosis cases in the United States. This disease, whose symptoms resemble a bad upset stomach, is caused by a small *Salmonella* bacterium that lives in the turtle's intestinal tract and multiplies readily in turtle-bowl water. It also infects the owners of many other animals, and is occasionally a contaminant of canned foods. The number of turtle-related cases, however, was sufficient to bring about a 1972 federal ban on interstate shipment of the southern ranch-bred baby turtles, and on the importation of any live turtles into the United States. The ranches in Mississippi and Louisiana are still operating primarily for foreign export purposes, although the enforcement of the federal and several state bans on the red-eared turtle is quite lax and the turtles can still be found in stores. Even with this setback, the vogue for reptilian pets is still very much on the rise.

IT is intriguing to indulge in some idle speculation about the origin of the odd love-hate relationship between reptiles and humans. The new popularity of reptile pets, like a little child's deep interest in them, is part bravado—a swelling pride in shedding a fear. Therefore, the source of the conquered fear is the thing that seems worth psychological attention. Some of man's horrified reaction to a particularly large, crawly reptile is traditional, either learned or affected. Part of it, however, may be innate. For a long time it has

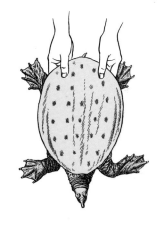

*Turtles that have long sturdy tails like the snapping turtle (above) can be picked up with a firm grasp of the tail, though prolonged handling in this way may injure them. But species with shorter tails, like the soft-shelled turtle shown below, are best handled by holding on to the back part of the upper shell. Although no turtle is venomous, many can inflict painful bites.*

been the habit of sages to deride the popular belief that the dread of snakes is instinctive. They point out that a baby does not recoil at a proffered snake; he accepts and chews on it joyously. But this means nothing: The same baby demonstrates no fear of open flame either. Humans have had a long evolutionary communion with serpents. There is growing evidence that a main center of human evolution was in a part of Africa where cobras, mambas and pythons are common today and likely have been for a long time. It is unthinkable that with such a background we should have failed to acquire any inherent snake-avoidance adaptations. It is even less likely that we should have wholly lost them.

That is to say, it seems pretty certain that a little of our fear of snakes is instinctive. The greater part of it no doubt comes from memories of the harrowing way Grandma took on over the whiteoak snake in the privy, and from hearing the tale embroidered in the third and fourth generation. But to say without proof that any ape has gotten over all its instinctive apprehension of the python's coils makes little sense. A dog goes around and around before lying down in the long-dead grass of a living-room rug—and an adult human mind whirls at the sudden sight of a snake.

At this stage in history, reptiles are not a major menace to human life. The most important reptilian causes of injury and death are crocodiles and poisonous snakes. In the Indian subcontinent, where people live cozily with cobras and kraits, there are some thousands of deaths by snake bite every year. Although hard figures for the South American continent are not available, snake bite is common in some areas, and despite the pioneering in serum therapy by a Brazilian laboratory, the Butantan Institute, fatalities are frequent in the back country of the American tropics. A number of the bigger crocodilians, including one of the caimans and the salt-water crocodile of Asia, are perversely unable to appreciate the special qualities of the human animal, and absentmindedly eat one from time to time. The Nile crocodile is the worst culprit in this respect, chiefly because of an almost ritual indifference on the part of women who wash clothes along East African lakes and rivers. They not only wash there, under the rapt gaze of cruising crocodiles, but actually turn their backs on the peril, clinging stubbornly to the ancestral custom of standing in the water and scrubbing the wash on a rock on the bank. It is folly to think crocodiles would ignore such an invitation and among villages in the southern part of the Great Rift Valley, on Lake Nyasa or along the Shire River, they often do not.

It seems a mark of curious forebearance on the part of crocodilians that in the rest of their range they eat so few people. In Florida, where the alligator reaches sizes and appetites big enough to engorge the largest humans, the potential hazard of these beasts was until recently mitigated by their quickly dwindling numbers. Then conservation authorities placed the animals on endangered species lists, and the protected alligators soon proliferated until they were as plentiful as ever. As their numbers grew back to natural levels, authorities were besieged with increasing numbers of complaints at the alligators' increasingly asocial behavior. One eight-foot (2.4-m) beast held up traffic at a busy intersection in Miami and attacked the officer sent to remove it; another killed a 16-year-old girl swimming alone in a lake at night. It has been noted, though, that the beasts that actually attacked humans came from areas where alligators were quite tame from incessant

**IGUANA STEW**

Catch a fat female iguana, preferably in March or April, kill it and skin it and remove the insides. Save the eggs, including the yellow ones, also the liver and heart. Dismember the body by cutting it down the backbone and dividing the sections in three parts and the legs in two. Place the pieces in a pot containing a little heated coconut oil and brown lightly over a low fire. Pour in enough water to cover the meat, and drop in a chile piquante and garlic to taste.

Meanwhile, in another pot of very salty water, boil the eggs in shells with a chile pod for half an hour. Drain them and add, shells and all, to the meat, along with the diced liver and heart and the yellow eggs. Now cook everything until the liquid has almost disappeared. Pour the remaining broth over red beans and rice, and heap the stewed meat on top.

contact with people. An alligator hand-fed on chicken legs by humans must be excused, scientists reason, if it makes an attempt on a human leg extended to it in precisely the same fashion. In this sense, indirectly or not, man probably provokes most of the alligators' attacks himself. Ross Allen of Silver Springs, Florida, confessed he was scared of his own tame bull alligators, but he cheerfully swam after and manhandled the wild ones.

In the mutual feeding relationship between men and reptiles, many more reptiles than men are eaten. As reptile food, man is nowadays not a significant item. If you lie nine days unfound on the bottom of a pond the little stinkjims may finally pick at you in a desultory way. But for a civilized man with his wits about him, being eaten by reptiles should not be a significant worry. Similarly, the majority of civilized people do not depend heavily on reptiles as food, although in one place or another about the earth man has always eaten reptiles of every kind.

Crocodilians appear on tables in various parts of their range. Crocodile meat is coarse, however, and to most Westerners confusingly intermediate in quality between fish and beef. Although it was at one time a regular part of the Seminole Indian diet, I have never heard an enthusiastic appraisal of alligator steak by anyone not either very hungry or trying hard to be open-minded. Most of the bigger lizards are hunted for food by indigenous folk, and at least one—the big tree iguana—is very toothsome game. On the Central American coast the Creoles cook a female iguana with her unlaid eggs in a way to make a gourmet cry with joy. The Japanese, whose culture is ancient and cuisine respectable, consume sea snakes in volumes that support a sizable industry.

Of all the reptiles it is the turtles that most notably have counted in human diets, both civilized and savage. Most primitive peoples who live in areas where turtles live eat them, and excavations show that this has always been so. In the rivers of northeastern South America turtles are a more important source of meat than any domesticated animal. In the lower Amazon the array of turtle dishes prepared constitutes almost a special endemic turtle cuisine. In China and Japan soft-shelled turtles are held in great and wholly deserved esteem, and the same genus has a few centers of popularity in the generally reptile-shy United States.

THE big herbivorous giant tortoises have in the past been an important staple for the crews of ships on long voyages in the eastern Pacific and Indian oceans. The statistics on the depredations of whaling vessels stopping at the Galápagos Islands during the 19th Century to take on giant tortoises are almost beyond belief. In the southeastern United States the gopher tortoise was a blessing to Indians and pioneers, and has remained so even to a few modern folk of advanced gastronomic criteria. A curious bit of ethnozoology is the culinary prestige of the salt-marsh terrapin *(Malaclemys terrapin)* in the United States during the three decades before the First World War. The terrapin somehow became a gastronomic status symbol.

The most important source of human food among reptiles is the green sea turtle. Clear green-turtle soup is a widely revered gourmet's dish, as is the meat of the green turtle, which has gained great popularity in recent years. The best parts of the turtle are the flippers, chine, calipee and calipash; the last three are the shell edge and the cartilaginous space filler in the lower and the upper shells, and these parts furnish the incomparable gelatinous texture

## TERRAPIN STEW

Of all the edible North American turtles, the diamondback terrapin of Chesapeake Bay is said to make the most delicious stew. Ways of making it are as varied as the localities they come from. The following is based on an old recipe from Chesterfield County, Virginia. One six- to seven-inch (15.2- to 17.8-cm) terrapin serves two. To kill, plunge into boiling, salted water. Parboil for one and a half hours until feet fall off and shell cracks. Remove the turtle and place on its back until cool enough to handle. Discard the heavy part of the intestines, gall and sand bags. Save the liver, small intestines and eggs along with the meat. Pick to pieces. (It is not necessary to bone terrapin.) Cover with boiling water and season highly with pepper, salt, cayenne pepper, hard-boiled egg and lemon. Stew until well done. Just before serving add at least one glass of champagne or sherry.

of turtle dishes. Calipee in particular is the essential ingredient of clear turtle soup. It is harvested mainly from marine turtles, because evolution has lightened their armor for aquatic life by partially suppressing their bone growth. During the early development of other species of turtles, bone fuses together into two solid shells, the carapace and the plastron, and even in sea turtles the spaces at each side of the upper shell tend to be closed by bone as the animal ages. The openings among the sea turtles' plastral bones remain, though, and throughout life are covered only by broad scales over an inner layer of cartilage. This cartilage is the calipee.

Gourmet chefs now make turtle soup from no more of the green turtle than calipee, which is a storable product easily obtained from beached turtles. The calipee is removed by slicing around the edges of the spaces it fills. The pieces thus taken are scraped, washed and dried in the sun. A 300-pound (136-kg) green turtle yields about six pounds (2.7 kg) of well-dried calipee.

The market for calipee is matched by an increasing world-wide demand for other reptile by-products. Carey, the shell of the hawksbill turtle, which craftsmen turn into burnished golden jewelry, has increased in price once more; there are rumors that the Japanese, for centuries the best of all tortoise-shell craftsmen, boosted the price. They are the only ones, I believe, who successfully weld it into blocks of any thickness with no sign of joint planes even in the honey-clear carey that they esteem so highly. The Japanese leather industry also has been increasingly turning to the world's crocodilians as a source of hides—and the tough, shiny, attractive lizard leather is eagerly sought for handbags, belts and shoes around the world. The garment industry can make use only of the belly and flank skin of the reptiles, since the hide on the back is so tough, and this relatively small yield of hide per beast killed has helped to decimate the world's crocodilian population in record time. By the mid-20th Century, environmentalists became aware of the serious plight of the beasts, and hastily imposed world-wide import-export regulations designed to protect the most endangered species. For many species, though, these regulations came too late, and many more, not yet formally endangered, are being harvested in quantities that ensure their eventual extinction too. Significantly, as crocodilian-hide trade is inhibited by the international endangered species codes, the leather industry has dealt increasingly in the less durable but still attractive snakeskin, perhaps heralding the approaching doom of that family as well.

ALL over the world there are foreboding signs that the long, placid association between reptiles and men may soon develop into a crisis. Man used to venerate his reptilian predecessors; now he covets them. The resurgence of the tortoise-shell industry is simply one of dozens of examples. During the 1940s, with the growth of the plastics industry, it seemed for a while that tortoise shell would become a worthless artifact of the past. The price of carey fell to almost nothing, and all over the Caribbean *careyeros* turned to other work. Now, though, their business is booming once again. I seriously doubt that the small world population of *Eretmochelys*—or many of their reptilian brothers—will long survive the unchecked spread of this commerce. Some countries, Costa Rica among them, have banned the hunting of the hawksbill and other countries have taken modest steps toward protecting various kinds of reptiles. But despite some encouraging signs, the pressures against the reptiles are mounting.

YOUNG CAIMANS SHOW ONE OF THE DEFENSIVE MEASURES OF THE CROCODILIANS: HIDING AS MUCH OF THEMSELVES IN WATER AS POSSIBLE

# Techniques for Survival

Not all of the reptiles are so formidably armored as the turtles, nor so fearsomely toothed as the crocodilians, nor so venomously fanged as many snakes. How, then, do the others take care of themselves? Their methods range from nimble retreats to Houdini escape acts and such ruses as pretending to be big or dead, the last so convincingly played by one snake that it goes through convulsions.

AN ANGRY TOAD-HEADED AGAMID LIZARD FROM ARABIA REARS UP ON ITS HAUNCHES, MOUTH OPEN MENACINGLY AND TAIL CURLED STIFFLY.

# Here One Moment, Gone the Next

To escape danger, many reptiles simply run away. Others hide in holes, under rocks and in similar inaccessible spots. A few, however, do not have retreats regularly available to them and must rely on such protective measures as threats and burrowing. The Arabian toad-headed lizard and the South African puff adder, both desert dwellers, bury themselves in sand to elude their enemies. But before wriggling underground, the spunky little lizard assumes a defensive stance and tries to bluff its attacker. If hard put, it will even bite, usually holding on so tightly that its jaws must be pried loose. Another desert lizard of the same family grimaces ferociously, expanding and reddening large folds of skin at the corners of its mouth.

Should the bluff fail, the lizard quickly buries itself by tilting its body from side to side and edging into the sand. At first it plows in with its sloping head, but once under the surface, it arches the neck upward and is in a position to crawl out again after

A SOUTH AFRICAN DWARF PUFF ADDER, RETREATING INTO THE SAND TAILFIRST, SHIMMIES TO SINK BELOW THE SURFACE. AS IT DESCENDS the enemy leaves. The horned lizard of the American Southwest buries itself in a similar manner, but often does so to get away from another enemy —the desert sun.

The dwarf puff adder, although equipped with fangs and venom glands that give the back of the head a swollen look, does not stand up to an enemy as the toad-headed lizard does, but wriggles into the sand immediately, leaving a ghost impression behind in the surface. It is aided in its downward retreat by scales which work the grains away from the bottom and sides of its thick body.

The dwarf puff adder's eyes are well protected from irritating grains of sand by the clear shields, or spectacles, covering them, found in all snakes. The toad-headed lizard does not have these shields, but does have scaly "eyebrows" which project out over its eyes, and long scales that fringe the eyelids and serve as lashes. Above ground, these "lashes" help keep wind-blown particles and dust out of the eyes.

*DRACO VOLANS*, A LIZARD OF SOUTHEAST ASIA, EXECUTES A G

## Fast Runners and Artful Gliders

Survival for many reptiles depends upon the speed
of their getaway. The American zebra-tailed and
collared lizards, clocked at 16 to 17 miles an hour
(25.7 to 27.4 km/h), are the fastest of their group.
Along with the crested dragon shown in the sequence
at left, they are among the few lizards to start off in
an upright position. Many other bipedal lizards begin at a trot and as they gain speed rise on their
long hind legs and bound off. Some bipedal lizards,
such as the Central American basilisk, can even take

**THE CRESTED DRAGON**, Australia's "bicycle lizard," restorts to
a bipedal gait when in a hurry; each stride is two-and-a-half
times the body length. The long tail acts as a counterbalance.

THE "WINGS" MAY BE YELLOW BELOW AND ORANGE AND BLACK ON TOP, OR BURNT UMBER WITH BLACK STRIPES AND MAROON EDGES

several steps on the surface of water before they fall in and swim. No modern reptiles can fly as could the extinct pterosaurs. The nearest they come to true flight is gliding, an art which one lizard genus, *Draco*, the flying dragons, has developed to a considerable state of refinement. Their "wings" are actually folds of scaly membrane supported by five or six pairs of ribs growing from their stick-thin bodies. With these flaps outspread, a *Draco* can glide more than 50 feet (15.2 m) between tree trunks.

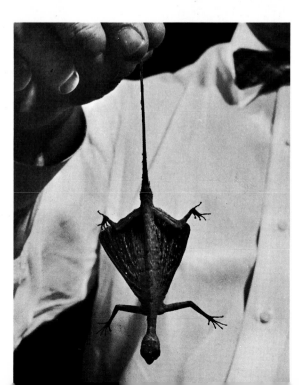

DANGLING from a human hand, a *Draco* reveals its small size. When crawling on a tree, it folds its colorful "wings" —and thus the narrow body looks green all over and blends with the bark.

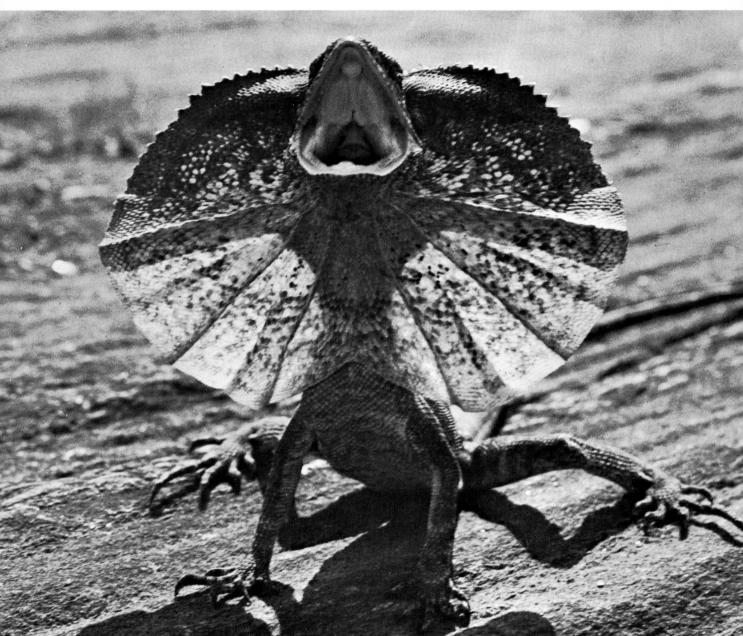

**THE FRILLED LIZARD** of Australia is shown in the photograph at upper left resting on a log as a tree snake glides up. In the next photograph, the lizard bobs up hissing and begins to un-furl its umbrella-like frill to scare an intruder. Extended *(below)*, the frill is yellow, scarlet and steel blue, and in an eight-inch-long (20.3-cm) specimen may be seven inches (17.8 cm) wide.

# The Intimidators

Several small, inadequately armed reptiles resort to bluffing as a defense. Horned lizards squirt blood, swell up and sometimes bite feebly or inflict wounds with their horns. The lizard opposite meets danger head on, erecting its frill, showing its teeth and occasionally even rearing on its hind legs in an attempt to bite. Other lizards swell brightly colored throat fans. Some bob up and down or rock back and forth.

**SPATTERED WITH BLOOD**, which it has just squirted from its own eye, a California horned lizard waits for the cornea to clear up. The blood may possibly irritate other animals' eyes.

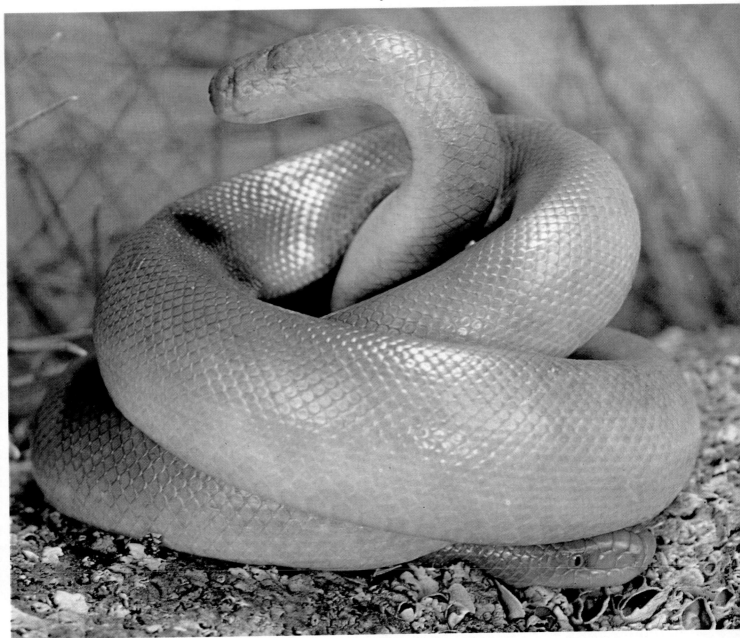

**WAVING A FALSE HEAD**, the rubber boa hides its real head among coils of its body. The decoy is actually the blunt tail. When threatened, this small, gentle snake, northernmost relative of the giant boas, rolls up into a protective ball with only the tail sticking out. An enemy will almost invariably bite the wrong end, as evidenced by the scars on this specimen's tail.

163

**FULL OF BRAVADO** when first confronted by an aggressor, the harmless eastern hog-nosed snake flattens its neck like a cobra, swells up, waves its tail and hisses loudly.

**WHEN ITS BLUFF FAILS,** a hog-nose plays dead. It turns on its back, its mouth wide open. To give such "deaths" a realistic touch, hog-noses will often fake convulsions.

**RAISING ITS HEAD,** a hog-nose peeks to see whether the enemy has left. If righted, it will promptly flop on its back in a limp pose, as though to prove it is still dead.

AT EASE on a leaf, the South African armadillo lizard bears some resemblance to a crocodile. But whereas the crocodile's scales are flat, the lizard's are spiked, especially along the tail.

## A Wound-Up Lizard

There is a mythical snake that can put its tail in its mouth and roll along like a hoop. But few people know that there is a real reptile—the armadillo lizard of South Africa—that has perfected such a position as a means of self-defense. And though this lizard cannot roll away over the veld, its projecting spiny scales form an effective stockade around its most vulnerable part—its soft-skinned belly.

When pursued, this slow-moving little lizard, often colored to blend with the sand, heads for a crevice in a rock. Once hidden, it sweeps its tail, which accounts for more than half its length, like a shield around the belly, usually stuffing the tip into its mouth, and lies there. Even a fairly strong pull is not likely to dislodge it. Unlike most lizards, it does not have the "breakaway" tail that they depend on for escape in emergencies. Its tail is firmly attached and will withstand a stiff yank before coming off.

ON THE DEFENSE, the armadillo lizard looks like a wreath. It holds its tail in its mouth with its forefeet, thus protecting the belly from any animals foolish enough to disregard the spines.

A GREEN TURTLE, leaving a trac-
tor-like trail in the sand, lumbers
toward the sea after laying her eggs
upbeach. Because of the effort needed to move her great weight, she
often stops and emits a great sigh.

# 8

# A Dubious Future

I<small>F</small> the world goes on the way it is going all its reptiles will one day be in
pens and cages. Some people might accept this calmly, but I mistrust the
prospect. Reptiles are a part of the old wilderness of earth, the environment
in which humans developed the attributes that make us human. If we let
reptiles go it is a sign we are ready to let all wilderness go. When that
happens we shall no longer be exactly human.

One of the awesome enigmas of today is how to slow the ruin of the natural
earth. The ironic fact is that population control is probably not far off. When
the spread of our species has been curbed and thoughtful descendants have
taken charge they will look about for what has been left of old values. One of
these values is what the human spirit gets from wilderness, from all kinds of
wild, original landscapes and beings. The way we are heading, what we keep
of the old earth will not be enough to save our honor with our descendants.

Reptiles are diminishing nearly everywhere. To keep them with us in
natural habitat will require dedication, sacrifice, and probably some luck as
well. Yet when people ask whether the situation is hopeless, whether the
hawksbill and the Atlantic ridley can be saved, whether there will be wild

crocodiles and snakes in the year 2100—when you face such questions squarely and start putting together the two sides of the prospect, you have to admit that there is hope, at least a little bit. The main hope is that people nowadays are more upset over the idea of losing species than they were a few years ago, and a thousand times more than back in the 1800s.

So what we have now is a race between the decline of reptiles and the spread of a feeling of obligation to keep them. This new concern over species' becoming extinct came over us unexpectedly. Rachel Carson's documentation of our degradation of the environment in *Silent Spring* turned a lot of people into active and vocal environmentalists. During the late 1960s and early 1970s there developed, along with our worry about abusing the landscape in general, a new stewardship for wild species—not just species of potential economic value, but all species.

In recent years whole landscapes have been saved from human encroachment and destruction because it was found that a scheme threatened a kind of bird or clam or minnow with extinction. Whatever future the wild species may have will come from the dominance of this concern over the frenzy for growth and development. Putting an obscure little snake or lizard on an endangered list is a worthy and useful move. Taking constructive action to save it is quite a different thing—particularly if the species involved has no conceivable influence on the material welfare of man.

As a resident of peninsular Florida, and one who has kept an affectionate eye on reptiles since my student days, I am saddened by the way they are dropping out of most Florida landscapes. And I am puzzled by it, too, because some species are dwindling without evident cause. In other cases, of course, the causes are clear—in the loss of some kinds of snakes for instance. Snakes are probably disappearing from this part of the country faster than any other group of vertebrates.

I N addition to being the object of widespread antipathy from man, snakes suffer from the draining of marshes, the reforestation of land in pure stands of unsuitable habitat, and the spreading of poisons that kill off the food supplies of the creatures snakes eat, and even kill the snakes themselves. But the most spectacular thing happening to snakes is the onslaught of cars on the roads. The worst snake traps are the causeways across marshes. Snakes move onto these to escape flooded or dried-out habitats, or merely in the course of foraging. I remember a vast killing of snakes once on the road across Paynes Prairie, when man and weather conspired against the creatures of the marsh. On October 18, 1941, a hurricane moved in from the Gulf, spun in the vicinity for 36 hours and brought 14 inches (35.6 cm) of rain in five days. The Prairie changed from marsh to lake and the water rose so high that only tips of the tallest grasses showed. On the 25th some students brought in 200 snakes they had caught along the road-fill and told of a great hegira of snakes, and of congregations of buzzards squabbling over the dead ones mashed by passing cars. There was clearly something extraordinary going on, and four of us from the Biology Department went out to investigate. We picked up a total of 723 snakes in two miles (3.2 km), and of these about two thirds were dead or had been injured.

As an accumulation over several days, this number of casualties would not have been unprecedented. But these were the accumulation of no more than the four hours or so since sundown; during the daylight hours buzzards had

## TWO IN A BURROW

*A sooty shearwater and a tuatara peer from a nesting burrow dug by the bird. These two animals often live together in harmony. Their cohabitation is made easy through much of the year by their routines: Usually the bird is off fishing during the day and the tuatara out foraging at night. When the bird migrates, the tuatara hibernates in the burrow.*

carried the dead snakes away almost as fast as they were run over. So the snakes we counted had all been killed after dark.

The first reptile to become an object of widespread concern was the green turtle, *Chelonia mydas*. It is not a really fair test of the conscience of mankind, because the green turtle is tragically good to eat and this has brought it to man's attention for a thousand years and more. It was once very abundant, but it has been overexploited, especially by international commerce, to the point that whole colonies have disappeared. The erosion was quite apparent and because the species was a potentially important resource, the predicament of sea turtles became the subject of widespread worry.

SINCE 1955, I have been involved in a campaign to rehabilitate the green turtle in the Caribbean Sea, where its once-extensive nesting range has been reduced to two rookery beaches. The decline evidently was due mainly to human depredations on the nesting grounds. Green turtles were killed as a ration for slaves, taken in hundreds as ships' stores by buccaneers and the British Navy, and eventually were carried to London to be made into soup for the Lord Mayor's Banquet.

In the early 1950s, the green turtle was facing complete extirpation from the Caribbean Sea. Then circumstances changed. In the first place, the suspected migratory feats of green turtles attracted scientific interest, and brought support from research foundations—the National Science Foundation and the Office of Naval Research—for studies of the complex life cycle of the species. Another factor motivating the intervention was the historic importance of the animal as human food, and its evident amenability to management, while serving as a harvester of great areas of marine vegetation that otherwise were going to waste. A final factor was the lucky circumstance that the single nesting beach remaining in the western Caribbean was located at Tortuguero, on the coast of the Republic of Costa Rica. Exploitation of the Tortuguero colony had brought Costa Rica a steady small revenue, in the form of a fee paid by a concessionaire who parceled out the beach to turtle-turners, and sold their catch to the Cayman Island schooners, or sent it away as deckloads on freight boats going back to Florida. In 1957 the government closed the beach to exploitation. This saved the green turtle for a while in the western Caribbean. It also deprived Costa Rica of all profit from the resource, while ironically helping other countries: Tortuguero populates pastures from Colombia to Mexico, especially those of the vast Miskito Bank off Nicaragua.

In 1955, when the first of a series of research grants to the University of Florida was made by the National Science Foundation, a tagging camp was established at Tortuguero. The information accumulated there soon stimulated the founding of the Caribbean Conservation Corporation, a nonprofit group dedicated to restoring the Atlantic green turtle in American waters. This was the strongest effort, I suppose, ever made in behalf of any reptile.

One aim of the organization was to re-establish breeding colonies in the places where they once were, by carrying batches of eggs or hatchlings to various introduction sites around the Caribbean Sea as well as in Florida and the Bahamas.

Eggs from Tortuguero beach were placed in artificial nests in a wire enclosure, where they were free of the usual hazards that attend incubation and hatching. After about two months the young turtles emerged and were placed in tanks of sea water and fed on chopped fish until distribution time. The United States Navy assisted in the distribution.

This project to create new colonies was a gamble at best. There was no way to be sure the planted hatchlings would go back to the introduction site when they reached maturity, instead of falling back into the ancestral cycle of reproductive travel and returning to Tortuguero. Unfortunately, there is no evidence that they actually returned to the new sites. And since there was no way known to tag the hatchlings durably, there was no way of knowing whether the hatchlings were wiped out by depredation in the new sites, or simply grew up and went back to Costa Rica to breed.

PERHAPS the most important factors favoring reptiles in their race against the spread of man and his works are the International Union for the Conservation of Nature (IUCN) and the closely allied World Wildlife Fund. One of IUCN's contributions to species survival is its *Red Data Book*. This gives basic information on species considered to be at any of three levels of insecurity: endangered (in immediate danger of extinction), vulnerable (evidently about to enter the endangered category), and rare (existing in small populations, and therefore unsafe). *Red Book* attention was first given reptiles and amphibians in 1968, and the list and synoptic accounts are periodically revised. In the 1975 listing, 73 species of reptiles are listed as endangered or vulnerable. The list is likely to become longer.

The role of the IUCN and the World Wildlife Fund does not include the exercise of regulatory power. These organizations can only advise and cajole, and provide funding for special applied research and management projects. But their work has had enormous effect. Governments all over the world are compiling their own inventories of their countries' endangered species, and passing laws to protect them.

In the United States, the Endangered Species Act of 1973 made it illegal to take, export or import species designated as endangered. The designating is mostly done by the Department of the Interior. Its 1976 list of endangered reptiles included 46 species.

Special attention has been given to species affected by international commerce. An auspicious development in the man-reptile relation was the 1973 Convention of International Trade in Endangered Species of Wild Fauna and Flora, at which 80 nations assembled to work out terms of a treaty to preserve wildlife. The participants agreed to adopt appropriate regulation, including a strict permit system, with periodic reports to the Convention Secretariat on permits issued.

The 85 reptiles listed by the Convention are involved in commerce in various ways. Some are sold for use in medical experiments, some go to zoos or pet stores. Others are shipped about the earth as hides, leather, meat, shell, soup, oil, stuffed specimens, or in almost any other shape you can think of. In some cases a very profitable commerce is involved. Regulating it would clearly be a complex matter.

For example, a problem almost as important to sea-turtle survival as roads and cars are to the world's snakes is that of incidental catch in the nets of fishermen who are not after turtles at all. Turtles have always been caught incidentally in trawls, pound nets and purse seines, but in the past this drain was of little importance. Turtle populations were bigger and nets, or trawls, were fewer and smaller—especially shrimp trawls, which are often dragged over foraging habitat of turtles, and which in the nesting season transgress the travel routes and gathering places of the migrants. But when shrimp became a high-priced luxury item, the trawls were made much larger than they used to be, and their hauls were extended. So without malice or intention the shrimpers took a serious toll from sea-turtle populations.

The most serious collision between turtles and trawlers involved a Mexican species, Kemp's ridley *(Lepidochelys kempi)*, whose nesting aggregations, or *arribadas*, near Rancho Nuevo on the Tamaulipas coast once numbered around 40,000. By the 1970s they comprised fewer than 4,000 turtles, and these arrived only in broken bands of 50 or so. This was the only existing breeding place of *kempi*. The colony there was the source of the dead ridleys that used to wash ashore in numbers along the Florida East Coast after encountering shrimp trawls there. Not many ridleys wash ashore there any longer, or anywhere else for that matter. The shrimpers admit that they no longer catch ridleys often and they seem to consider this change favorable. It is not. The ridleys are not caught because they are almost gone.

It is theoretically possible to devise a deflector panel or baffle that, placed across the mouth of a trawl net, would let shrimp in and keep out big objects such as turtles. Intensive work on such a device is badly needed. The shrimpers favor the idea. They dislike the public resentment when people find dead turtles on the beach. And they do not like to catch turtles at all, because the heavy hard-shelled load damages the shrimp in the net. So there is no opposition to the project—only insufficient motivation and effort.

ONE way to save endangered species is to study their ecology, behavior and population levels in the field and thus collect information for use in coping with their troubles. Such attention introduces an important side benefit also: the so-called "scientific presence" factor. When zoologists enter an area to investigate the status of a wild species, the government involved usually becomes solicitous and may take steps to protect the species.

An organization that is making outstanding contributions in this way is the New York Zoological Society, which has embarked on a program of studies of vulnerable species of animals whose ecology is poorly known. A number of these are reptiles. Because there is never enough money to do everything, the Society chose to concentrate its attention on certain groups. One of these is the carnivores, and accordingly many of the projects have involved crocodilians. The Crocodilia are in bad shape the world over; because their hides bring high prices in world trade, it is going to require a major effort and much more knowledge of crocodilian ecology than we now have to save some of them. The Society has nine crocodilian projects under way in various parts of the vast range of the group.

Another group of beleaguered reptile carnivores that have been the object of major attention from the Society are the monitors. With grants from the Society, Dr. Walter Auffenberg spent two long periods of field work on Komodo Island, home of the Komodo dragon. For a total of 18 months Dr. Auffenberg, for much of the time accompanied by his wife and son, literally lived with the dragons. Through a well-planned program of tagging, radio-tracking and systematic observation, he pieced together a fascinating picture of their behavioral ecology, proving among other things that though the mature dragon is too heavy to climb a tree, the young are regularly arboreal. And the common belief that Komodo monitors feed only on carrion is not

## THE HELPFUL BIRDS

*The tuatara's existence on its remote islands is made possible by sea birds like the cormorants shown above. They cover the ground and rocks with their droppings, creating an ideal environment for the development of a large population of ground insects such as beetles and crickets. These are the tuatara's main source of food, and it forages for them at night (below).*

true; the big ones can and do occasionally kill and consume cattle. Dr. Auffenberg's pioneering studies provide the information needed for managing and maintaining remaining populations of this unique and exciting animal—and of other beleaguered monitors as well.

One effort to farm crocodilians offers an interesting solution to the demand for alligator and crocodile skins. Launched in New Guinea, the project involves a vast system of little government-sponsored cottage-industry and community-operated crocodile farms, stocked from wild populations. The stock is fed on fish caught locally. The government gives the farmers small grants to establish the farms and gets good public relations in turn. The people have taken naturally to the work and, with hides bringing up to $16.50 a square foot (0.1 m²) (an average of $115 each), even a small enterprise is an important source of revenue. According to proponents of the scheme, moderate harvesting of wild hatchlings does no harm; more important, it motivates people to preserve natural wet country they would otherwise clamor to have drained. The program also curbs poaching and smuggling, they say; because these pursuits are clearly contrary to community welfare, local strictures are tougher than those of the central government.

Thus, in New Guinea the idea of banning world trade in crocodile hides collides head-on with what in one way seems a creative and promising scheme to help poor people, and at the same time to protect wild habitat. The IUCN crocodile group decided that the protection the New Guinea system generates for the habitat, as well as for the species, is too important to lose, despite the fact that it encourages the world market for crocodile leather. They even proposed transplanting the New Guinea system to other crocodilian landscapes, particularly those of South America. If this ethic of saving wilderness by taking from it only what it can stand to lose could everywhere be substituted for intemperate abuse, then the trade-off would certainly be worth considering. But the ultimate question is: How many species of crocodilians will remain by the time that ethic has spread widely?

THE most surprising advance in reptile conservation is the recovery of the American alligator. Not long ago alligators seemed to be doomed as a feature of the natural landscape. Then they were listed as an endangered species and given some fairly effective protection and, wherever any of their old range and habitat were left unspoiled, they came back in gratifying numbers. They have been removed from the list of endangered species.

Ten years ago the comeback of the American alligator would have seemed impossible, especially in Florida. We used to spend a lot of time grieving over losing the alligator in Florida. I would go over to Jonah's Pond and look at the alligators there, and think how poor the world would be when there was no place a private citizen could go and see wild alligators. Jonah's Pond is one of the solid assets of the University of Florida. It is a sinkhole lake with a marsh at one end and open water at the other, and all through it a grand confusion of marsh creatures and floating and emergent plants. The place is a relic of a vanishing past; incredibly, it lies on a university campus with 28,000 students, less than half a mile (0.8 km) from where I am writing now.

I remember going over one time to where an alligator called Crooked-jaw used to build her nest. That year it was beside a wire fence, at one edge of the swampy end of the lake. I walked over to the nest and looked at it closely. I had photographed it the day before, and I could see that Crooked-jaw had made some changes during the night. They were not drastic—just small, fastidious adjustments to show she knew the heap was warming a new generation of her kind. A root-mass of buttonbush had been added, and a few live switches of *Decodon*, and some scooped-up slush of coontail from the bottom. Atop the pile was a single balled-up pink paper towel; and though it seems unlikely, I knew I had seen it lying six feet (1.8 m) from the nest the day before. I had been aroused at the sight of it, at the idea of anybody defiling the premises of an alligator with pink. Crooked-jaw clearly failed to share my resentment. There is no accounting for tastes. The nest did not look as good to me with the paper towel on it, but the matter was not in my hands.

The alligator was not in her usual station, her lying-in pool, as it were—the little dredged-out hole of water that a mother gator waits in while her eggs are incubating. This time she was off somewhere among the floating islands. I started croaking, *eer-rump, eer-rump,* like a little gator croaking. A little way out through the flooded willows a floating island began to quake; and then all at once water surged up under the frogbit raft beside the waiting pool, and Crooked-jaw came up looking at me. A gallinule whined from a bonnet patch, and in the high haze to the west the sand-hill cranes were bugling. I croaked some more, but the alligator had lost interest. She sank into the water till her chin rested on the mud, and only the bumps of her eyes and nose and the big scales of her back stuck out.

Looking at her in her fragment of seminatural landscape, I was sure again that the primitive earth must be saved, and that this preservation must be done without attempts to justify it on practical grounds. Species and wild landscapes must be kept because it pleases people to contemplate them, and because humans of future times will be appalled if we carelessly let them go.

THE tuatara of New Zealand gives one the frightening feel of the precarious hold that useless wild things have on the world. This loneliest reptile in the world, known technically as *Sphenodon punctatus,* looks like a stocky, big-headed lizard. The males average about two feet (61 cm) long and weigh about two pounds (907 g). Females are a good deal shorter and only half as heavy. The common name, "tuatara," is a Maori word that means "spiny," and refers to a low, toothed crest down the neck and back. A few hundred years ago there were tuataras on mainland New Zealand, and the Maoris ate them. Today they live only on some 20 cliff-bound islets off the New Zealand coast, one of the smallest geographic ranges of any vertebrate animal.

Although *Sphenodon* looks like a lizard, it clearly is not. It differs from lizards in many ways. One of the most arresting is the lack of any copulatory organ. Even more engrossing, to the paleontologist at least, is the presence of two complete bony arcades in the skull's temporal region, as in the ancient diapsid reptiles. Evidence suggests that the open-sided skull of lizards probably is a modification of this old two-arcade style. So the tuatara seems to fade back into the ancestral line of lizards and snakes. The wonder is how little it changed in the millions of years lizards and snakes were evolving.

One of the features of *Sphenodon* that used to be considered distinctive is a third, or median, eye, located on top of the head but roofed over by skin. Although this organ has the lens, retina and nerve connections that go with light-reception, there are no eye muscles or other apparatus for focusing, and experiments indicate that no seeing is done with the eye. Its function, if it still has any, is thus unknown. In any case, the median eye is not peculiar to

*Sphenodon.* It occurs in various modern lizards too, and may be used by them in their behavioral temperature control. In some fossil reptiles it was much more strongly developed and perhaps used for vision.

The female tuatara lays from eight to 15 soft-shelled eggs, each just over an inch (2.5 cm) long. The nest is a pit in well-drained soil, dug and covered by the female. The period of incubation is 15 months, which is far longer than that of most other reptiles. The tuatara is one of the rare reptiles with a true voice and has been heard to croak dolefully on misty nights or on becoming annoyed with a captor. It seems to take 20 years to reach sexual maturity. This, and the slow growth rates that have been recorded, lead to the belief that it may attain ages of a century or more.

The tuatara today is mainly insectivorous and nocturnal. It has been observed foraging in temperatures as low as 45° F. (7.2° C.). It lives in intimate association with the sea birds that swarm on the islands. The birds keep the underbrush broken down and manure the soil heavily, and an abundant insect fauna lives in it. One of the bird associates, a petrel, digs burrows. The tuatara regularly occupies these, sometimes moving in before the petrel is through incubating eggs or raising chicks.

The sparse tuatara community reveals ecologic relationships with singular clarity. Although the long-term survival of the tuatara may never be explained, it is easy to see why the creature is able to hold on now. Its inaccessible islands, with their bird colony and salt-forest habitat, are a remote asylum where an ancient type, elsewhere replaced by more nimble lizards and mammals, can live on in ancestral ways.

The one defect in its case as a triumph of wilderness preservation is that the effort involved in saving it should have been so slight. Saving the tuatara required only laws protecting the animal itself, and the removal of a few sheep that hurt the habitat. Thus, it is a poor prototype. No significant preserving of nature can be done with only slight sacrifice.

WHEN New Zealand set up the *Sphenodon* preserve I wish they had said that they had done it so plain men could go on singing the tuataras out of their holes. Looking for old accounts of the tuatara in New Zealand, I found this in a 1903 issue of the *Lyttelton Times*, quoted by James Hutton and Frederick Wollaston Drummond in their book, *The Animals of New Zealand:*

"The tuatara lizards at the Opaiva fisheries seem to be susceptible to music. They will come out of their holes to hear a song, when nothing else will induce them to appear. They prefer a good rousing chorus rather than a solo. Some time ago a number of visitors to the hatcheries wanted to see the tuataras, which, however, refused to come forth until a little girl sang 'Soldiers of the Queen,' and others joined in the chorus. The sound seemed to have appealed to the reptiles, and they responded by showing themselves to the singers."

Basically, what we have to do is go ahead and admit that tuataras must be saved so that people can sing them out of holes. Only then are we ready for the harder jobs, like justifying a future for snakes, which have no legs, hear no music and badly clutter subdivisions. Get to the core of what is required and we discover that it is an aggressive stewardship of relics, of samples of original order, of objects and organizations of cosmic craft. This work will necessitate the care and consideration of staunch people, and the reptile can be the test by which they are judged.

A LONE, FULLY GROWN TUATARA, PERHAPS A CENTURY OLD, CROAKS ITS PLAINTIVE SONG FROM THE SAFETY OF ITS BLEAK ISLAND REFUGE

# Twilight of the Reptiles

It has taken some 150 million years of paleontological disasters to reduce the immense diversity of reptilian life to a meager four orders. But it has taken man only a few hundred years of indiscriminate slaughtering to bring many survivors to the brink of complete extinction. Belatedly, in some areas of the world, conservationists are now studying ways to save these relics of the distant past.

## Chosen for Survival

Because they are no longer eaten and their hides have no commercial value, and because they inhabit clusters of remote islands which neither men nor other large predators want, the less than 10,000 remaining tuataras enjoy the protection of conservationists. But the species also has its own formidable survival equipment. This includes the ability to keep active at extremely low body temperatures, an adaptation well suited to its cool climate, and a relatively low metabolism, which means it can get along on a reduced diet—usually insects, worms and snails.

A MATURE MALE weighs about two pounds (907 g) and reaches a length of two feet (61 cm); adult females are shorter and much lighter. Handlers need not fear; tuataras are harmless to man.

CLOAKED IN GLOOM, Stephens Island is the most thoroughly studied habitat of tuataras. A square mile of cloud-capped land, it rises in sheer cliffs 1,000 feet (305 m) above Cook Strait in New Zealand.

TAIL REGENERATION, which tuataras share with many lizards, takes several years. A broken tail *(top)* will replace itself with a tail of a different texture *(center)* or, occasionally, with a forked tail *(bottom)*.

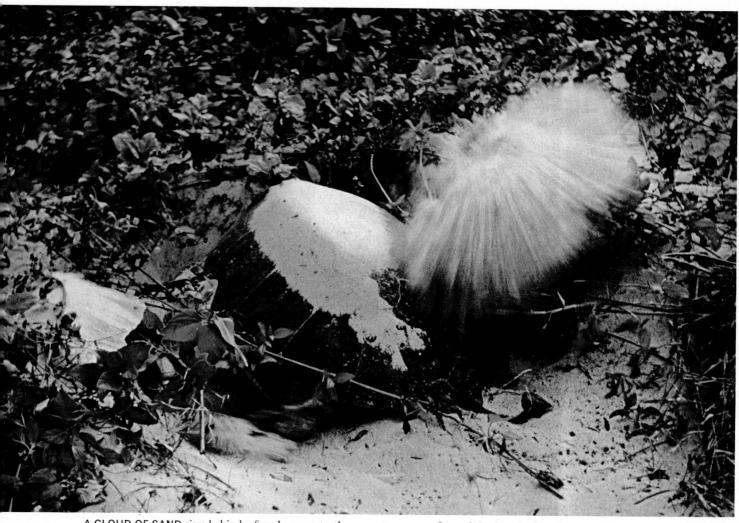

A CLOUD OF SAND rises behind a female green turtle excavating her nest on an Australian Great Barrier Reef beach. She excavates with all four flippers until her shell is level with the surface of the beach. She then uses her rear flippers to dig a deeper hole for her eggs. Since her eggs are prized by the local population, many will not be incubated long enough to hatch.

A COUPLE OF HATCHLINGS scramble out of the nest. They must now run a perilous gantlet to the sea while hungry birds swoop down upon them and predaceous fishes wait below.

## Candidates for Extinction

Unlike the tuatara, some aquatic turtles have been fair game for hunters for centuries. Across the Pacific, islanders harvest turtle eggs for their own food, and in the Caribbean turtles are killed for their meat, much of which is turned into soup. Demand for turtle leather and "tortoise-shell" (actually turtle-shell) ornaments claims still more. Since the animals are most vulnerable at their nesting grounds, some beaches are now official preserves. Studies of nesting habits, underway at research stations such as the University of Florida's Tortuguero camp in Costa Rica *(pages 184-185)*, are part of a broad effort to make sure that the sea-turtles' long history is not concluded.

A BUTCHERED FEMALE has her egg clusters removed and placed inside a tin can by a native of the island of Mer, near New Guinea. Both the meat and eggs are highly prized by the people of the southwest Pacific. On the little island of Talang Talang off Borneo, for example, it has been estimated that close to two million turtle eggs have been collected in a single year.

**ENTANGLED IN A NET** laid by Miskito Indian turtlemen off the coast of Nicaragua, this rare hawksbill turtle will soon drown. The Indians used to capture turtles only for their own food, but now they find such eager markets for their catches in the jewelry, leather and gourmet-food industries that a large portion of the world's sea-turtle population is being threatened by destruction.

**HOISTED BODILY** from its nesting beach in the Republic of Guyana, a hawksbill turtle is carried off by a local entrepreneur. This species is prized for its meat and for its delicately mottled shell, from which all genuine "tortoise-shell" jewelry is made.

**GRISLY REMAINS** of slaughtered olive ridley turtles pave a stretch of land flanking a nesting beach in Guerrero, Mexico. Poachers peel off only the valuable neck and flipper skin of the nesting ridleys for leather, and leave the rest of the carcass there to rot.

**MEASURING A TURTLE,** a graduate student and her assistant check on its growth rate for the Tortuguero Research Program in Costa Rica. To assist the study of green turtles, this beach was made a preserve.

**WEIGHING A TURTLE** that has just laid a clutch of eggs, scientists document the dramatic weight losses nesting turtles sustain. Females eat nothing during their nesting season, which may last for several months.

**THE AUTHOR**, who is director of the Tortuguero program, squats beside a tagged female turtle. By observing individual turtles, scientists can tell how often each female nests during her stay at Tortuguero, where she goes when she leaves and how often she returns. Only when their migration habits are known can rational steps be taken to save this endangered species.

# Bibliography

## General Herpetology

Bellairs, Angus d'A., *The Life of Reptiles*. Weidenfeld and Nicolson, London, 1969.

Goin, Coleman J. and Olive B., *Introduction to Herpetology*. W. H. Freeman, 1971.

Grzimek, Bernhard, *Grzimek's Animal Life Encyclopedia*, Volume 6: *Reptiles*. Van Nostrand and Reinhold, 1975.

Oliver, James, *The Natural History of North American Amphibians and Reptiles*. Van Nostrand, 1955.

Peters, James A., *Dictionary of Herpetology*. Hafner, 1964.

Pope, Clifford H., *The Reptile World*. Alfred A. Knopf, 1955.

Porter, Kenneth R., *Herpetology*. W. B. Saunders, 1972.

Schmidt, Karl P., and Robert F. Inger, *Living Reptiles of the World*. Doubleday, 1957.

## Evolution and Fossils

Colbert, Edwin H., *Evolution of the Vertebrates*. John Wiley & Sons, 1969.

Desmond, Adrian J., *The Hot-blooded Dinosaurs*. Dial Press, 1976.

Romer, Alfred S., *Vertebrate Paleontology*. University of Chicago Press, 1966.

Swinton, W. E., *Fossil Amphibians and Reptiles*. British Museum of Natural History, 1965. *The Dinosaurs*. John Wiley & Sons, 1970.

## Crocodilians

Graham, Alistair, and Peter Beard, *Eyelids of Morning: The Mingled Destinies of Crocodiles and Men*. New York Graphic Society, 1973.

Guggisberg, C. A. W., *Crocodiles. Their Natural History, Folklore and Conservation*. Wren Publishing, Victoria, 1972.

McIlhenny, E. A., *The Alligator's Life History*. Christopher, 1935.

Neill, Wilfred T., *The Last of the Ruling Reptiles: Alligators, Crocodiles, and their Kin*. Columbia University Press, 1971.

## Snakes and Lizards

Dunson, William A., ed., *The Biology of Sea Snakes*. University Park Press, 1975.

Fitch, Henry S., *Reproductive Cycles in Lizards and Snakes*. University of Kansas Museum of Natural History, 1970.

Klauber, Laurence M., *Rattlesnakes*, Vols. I and II. University of California Press, 1956.

Oliver, James A., *Snakes in Fact and Fiction*. Macmillan, 1958.

Pitman, Charles R. S., *A Guide to the Snakes of Uganda*. Wheldon & Wesley, 1974.

Pope, Clifford H., *The Giant Snakes*. Alfred A. Knopf, 1961.

Smith, Hobart M., *Handbook of Lizards of the United States and Canada*. Comstock, 1946.

Underwood, Garth, *A Contribution to the Classification of Snakes*. British Museum of Natural History, 1967.

U.S. Navy Bureau of Medicine and Surgery, *Poisonous Snakes of the World*. U.S. Government Printing Office, 1968.

Wright, Albert H. and Anna A., *Handbook of Snakes of the United States and Canada*. Comstock, 1957.

## Turtles

Bustard, Robert, *Sea Turtles: Their Natural History and Conservation*. Taplinger, 1973.

Carr, Archie, *Handbook of Turtles of the United States, Canada, and Baja California*. Comstock, 1952. *So Excellent a Fishe: A natural history of sea turtles*. Natural History Press, 1967.

Ernst, Carl H., and Roger W. Barbour, *Turtles of the United States*. University Press of Kentucky, 1972.

Pope, Clifford H., *Turtles of the United States and Canada*. Alfred A. Knopf, 1939.

Pritchard, Peter C. H., *Living Turtles of the World*. T. F. H. Publications, 1967.

Rebel, Thomas P., *Sea Turtles and the Turtle Industry of the West Indies, Florida, and the Gulf of Mexico*. University of Miami Press, 1974.

Wermuth, H., and R. Mertens, *Schildkröten, Krokodile, Bruchenechsen*. Gustav Fischer, Jena, 1961.

## Regional Guides

Cogger, Harold G., *Reptiles and Amphibians of Australia*. A. H. & A. W. Reed, London, 1975.

Conant, Roger, *A Field Guide to Reptiles and Amphibians of Eastern and Central North America*. Houghton Mifflin, 1975.

Deraniyagala, P. E. P., *A Colored Atlas of Some Vertebrates from Ceylon*, Vols. 2 and 3. Ceylon Government Press, 1953.

Donoso-Barros, Roberto, *Reptiles de Chile*. Ediciones de la Universidad de Chile, 1966.

Gharpurey, K. G., *The Snakes of India and Pakistan*. Popular Book Depot, Bombay, 1954.

Hellmich, Walter, *Reptiles and Amphibians of Europe*. Blanford Press, London, 1962.

Khalaf, Kamel T., *Reptiles of Iraq with Some Notes on the Amphibians*. Ar-Rabitta Press, Baghdad, 1959.

Leviton, Alan, *Reptiles and Amphibians of North America*. Doubleday, 1974.

Loveridge, Arthur, *Reptiles of the Pacific World*. Macmillan, 1946.

Mertens, Robert, and Heinz Wermuth, *Die Amphibien und Reptilien Europas*. Kramer, Frankfurt, 1960.

Peters, James A., and Braulio Orejas-Miranda, *Catalogue of the Neotropical Squamata*. Smithsonian Institution Press, 1970.

Schwartz, Albert, and Richard Thomas, *A Checklist of West Indian Amphibians and Reptiles*. Carnegie Museum of Natural History, 1975.

Smith, Hobart M., and Ernest Taylor, *Herpetology of Mexico: Annotated Checklists and Keys to the Amphibians and Reptiles*. Eric Lundberg, 1966.

Smith, Malcom, *The British Amphibians and Reptiles*. Collins, London, 1951.

Stebbins, Robert C., *A Field Guide to Western Reptiles and Amphibians*. Houghton Mifflin, 1966.

## Miscellaneous

Buchere, Wolfgang, Eleanor E. Buckley and Venancio Deulofeu, eds., *Venomous Animals and their Venoms*, Vols. 1 and 2. Academic Press, 1968.

Catalogue Committee of the Society for the Study of Amphibians and Reptiles, *Catalogue of American Amphibians and Reptiles*. SSAR, 1971.

Darlington, Philip J., Jr., *Zoogeography*. John Wiley & Sons, 1957.

Eibl-Eibesfeldt, I., *Ethology: The Biology of Behavior*. Holt, Rinehart & Winston, 1970.

Honegger, Rene E., ed., *Red Data Book: Amphibians and Reptiles*. International Union for the Conservation of Nature, Morges, 1968.

Minton, Sherman A., ed., *Snake Venoms and Envenomation*. Marcel Dekker, 1971.

Minton, Sherman A. and Madge R., *Giant Reptiles*. Charles Scribner's Sons, 1973.

Neill, Wilfred T., *Reptiles and Amphibians in the Service of Man*. Bobbs-Merrill, 1974.

## How to Care for Reptiles

Hoke, John, *Turtles and their Care*. Franklin Watts, 1970.

Smith, Hobart M., *Snakes as Pets*. T. F. H. Publications, 1965.

Villiard, Paul, *Reptiles as Pets*. Doubleday, 1969.

Worden, A. N., and W. Lane-Petter, eds., *The UFAW Handbook on the Care and Management of Laboratory Animals*. Universities Federation for Animal Welfare, London, 1957.

# Credits

*The sources for the illustrations in this book are shown below.*

*Credits for pictures from left to right are separated by commas, top to bottom by dashes.*

Cover—Nina Leen
8—Allan Grant
10—Lowell Hess
11—Matt Greene
12—Lowell Hess
13—Rene Martin
14, 15—Eva Cellini
17—Z. J. Leszczyneki
18, 19—Jack J. Kunz
20, 21—John Markham, James R. Simon from Photo Researchers, Inc.—John Gerard from National Audubon Society
22, 23—Russ Kinne from Photo Researchers, Inc.—Maitland A. Edey, Dmitri Kessel
24—Richard G. Zweifel
25—John H. Tashjian—N. Cohen
26, 27—Lisa Larsen, Harold Pollock from Freelance Photographers Guild—Dr. Robert S. Simmons
28, 29, 30—N. Cohen
31—R. Van Nostrand for the San Diego Zoo
32, 33—Matt Greene, John Markham
34—Herbert Gehr
36, 38, 39—Stephen Rogers Peck
40, 41—Sy Barlow
43—Walter Sanders
44, 45—Lowell Hess
46, 47—Drawings by Mark A. Binn courtesy American Museum of Natural History

48, 49—Mark A. Binn courtesy American Museum of Natural History except top Walter Sanders
50, 51—Courtesy American Museum of Natural History
52—Isabelle Hunt Conant
55—Frances W. Zweifel
56, 59—Matt Greene
60—John Norris Wood
63—Loomis Dean
64, 65—Carl Gans, Dr. Robert S. Simmons
66, 67, 68—Nina Leen
69—Nina Leen—Lee Boltin
70, 71—Nina Leen
72—Jay Leviton from Black Star
73—Bernard Hoffman—Walker Van Riper
74, 75—Rene Martin
76, 77—Paul Popper except right Carl Gans
78—Raymond Bridgman Cowles
80—Matt Greene
82—Rene Martin
84, 85—Frances W. Zweifel
87—Rene Martin
89—John Mitchell
90, 91—Painting by Mel Brindle
92—Loomis Dean
93—Lee Boltin
94—Loomis Dean—William Vandivert
95—Loomis Dean—William Vandivert
96, 97—N. Cohen—Bucky

Reeves, Loomis Dean
98—John Mitchell—Walter Dawn
99—R. Van Nostrand for the San Diego Zoo
100, 101—Isabelle Hunt Conant
102—John Gerard from Monkmeyer Press Photo Service
103—Denis Brihat from Rapho-Guillumette
104—Fred Ward from Black Star
106—Stephen Rogers Peck
108, 109—John Norris Wood
110—No credit
115—Russ Kinne from Photo Researchers, Inc.
116—Shelley Grossman—Nina Leen
117—Shelley Grossman—Alfred Eisenstaedt
118—Shelley Grossman
119—H. G. Cogger, Larry Burrows
120—N. Cohen
121—H. Heusser
122—Shelley Grossman except top Francis Miller
123—Francis Miller
124—Fritz Goro
126—Hans Zillessen
131—Eva Cellini
133—Mark A. Binn
135—Combine
136—G. E. Kirkpatrick for the San Diego Zoo

137—Walter Dawn
138, 139—Charles H. Hackenbrock, Archie Carr—Dr. Robert S. Simmons
140, 141—Mel Hunter
142, 143—Wolfgang Bayer
144, 145—Dr. Robert S. Simmons
146—Pierre Boulat
149—Enid Kotschnig
152, 153—Matt Greene
157—Annan Photo Features
158, 159—top Standard Oil Co., N. J.; bottom Mertens
160, 161—Peter Stackpole except left R. C. Snyder
162—Fritz Goro
163—John H. Tashjian—N. Cohen
164, 165—Richard G. Zweifel except right Nina Leen
166—Cy La Tour, N. Cohen
168—Fritz Goro
170, 173—Hans Zillessen
174, 175—Stephen Rogers Peck
177, 178, 179—W. H. Dawbin and M. D. King
180—Fritz Goro—Photo Mahuzier
181—Fritz Goro
182—Bernard Nietschmann
183—Peter C. H. Pritchard
184—Archie Carr—Jeanne A. Mortimer
185—Jo Conners

# Acknowledgments

The editors of the revised edition of *The Reptiles* are particularly indebted to John Behler, Curator, Department of Herpetology, New York Zoological Society; Sidney Horenstein, Scientific Assistant, Department of Fossil and Living Invertebrates, American Museum of Natural History; Peter Prichard, Florida Audubon Society.

For assistance with the original edition of this book the editors are also indebted to Charles M. Bogert, Chairman and Curator, Department of Herpetology, The American Museum of Natural History; Nathan W. Cohen, Head, Letters and Science Extension, University of California Extension at Berkeley; Edwin H. Colbert, Curator, Department of Vertebrate Paleontology, The American Museum of Natural History; Raymond B. Cowles, Professor Emeritus of Zoology, University of California at Los Angeles; W. H. Dawbin, Senior Lecturer on Zoology, University of Sydney, Australia; Herndon Dowling, Curator of Reptiles, New York Zoological Park; James A. Fowler, Assistant Professor of Biological Sciences, State University of New York at Stony Brook; Carl Gans, Professor of Biology, State University of New York at Buffalo; Carl K. Kauffield, Curator of Reptiles, Staten Island Zoo; Samuel McDowell, Associate Professor of Zoology, Rutgers University; Alfred S. Romer, Alexander Agassiz Professor of Zoology, Harvard University; Charles E. Shaw, Curator of Reptiles, San Diego Zoological Garden; Richard C. Snyder, Professor of Zoology, University of Washington; Walter Dawn; John N. Hamlet; Bucky Reeves; Robert S. Simmons, D.D.S.; Charles J. Stine, D.D.S.; John H. Tashjian and the New Zealand Consulate General, New York City; Richard G. Zweifel, Curator, Department of Herpetology, The American Museum of Natural History.

# Index

*Numerals in italics indicate a photograph or painting of the subject mentioned.*

Leopard lizard, *90-91*
*Lepidochelys kempi. See* Kemp's ridley
*Leptotyphlops phenops*, burrowing snake, 58
*Liodytes*, swamp snake, 114
Live birth, 113, 125-126; of aquatic reptiles, 107, 108, 113, 119, 126, 134; of boas, 14; of "typical" snakes, 15
Lizards, 9, 11-13, *26-27*, 99; anatomical characteristics of, 12, 19; aquatic, 106, 112, 114, *117;* arboreal, 12, 58, 83, *92-93,* 96, 112, 173; bipedal, *160;* burrowing, 13, *28-31,* 83; camouflage and color changes, *92-93;* classification of, 12-13; courtship and mating behavior, 127, 128, 136, *137;* eggs of, 130; evolution of, 42, *chart* 44-45; evolutionary relationship to snakes, 39; eyes of, 12, 39, *94-95,* 159, 175-176; feeding habits of, 54-55, 57, 58; foot adaptations of, *96-97;* gliding, 57, 83, *160-161;* hearing of, 12; leather from, 156; legless, 39, 79 *(see also* Worm lizards*)*; live-bearing, 125, 126; loss of tail, 12, *13;* molting of, 26, 85; number of existing species, *graph* 10, 26; parental behavior among, 132, 139; parthenogenesis among, 127; poisonous, 59; reproduction in, 12, 126; salt gland in, 107; sand-swimming, 83; scales of, 12; size range of, 12; vs. snakes, anatomical differences, 12; as social parasites of ants and termites, 84, 86; subterraneous *(see* Worm lizard*)*; vagility of, 81-82; waste elimination of, 19, 107. *See also* separate species of lizards
Locomotion: evolutionary progress, 37; flight, *38,* 39-40, 83; foot adaptations, *96-97;* gliding and parachuting, 83, *160-161;* of snakes, 25, 39, *diagrams* 84-85, *100-101;* of turtles, 20, 21; in water, 20, 39, 106, 107, 109, *116-117*
*Lophura amboinensis*, lizard, 112
Lung, 19; evolution of, 35, 36-37
*Lyttelton Times*, 176

M adagascar, 152
*Malaclemys terrapin*, 155
Mamba, snake, 15, 69, 154
Mammal-like reptiles, 38, 40-41, 42
Mammals, 42, 85, 125; evolution of, *38,* 40-41, *chart* 44; return to sea, analogies with reptiles, *41,* 106, 107
Man: danger from reptiles, 22, 69, 152, 153, 154-155; exploitation of reptiles for food, 155-156, 171, 172, 180, *181-183;* fear of snakes, 12, 154. *See also* Mythology
Marine iguanas, 12, 114, 116, *117*
Marine reptiles, 107, 112. *See also* Aquatic reptiles; Sea snakes; Sea turtles
Matamata, 11, 56-57, *122-123*
Mating, 86; copulation, 126, 127; courtship, 127-128; rivalry of males, 127, 128-130, *136-137;* of subterranean reptiles, enigma of, 84; use of Jacobson's organ in, 61, 127

Medicinal uses of reptiles, 152
Mesosaurs, *chart* 44-45
Mesozoic, 40, 41, 42, *chart* 44-45, 50, 83, 111; time scales for, *chart* 37
Mexican beaded lizard, 59
Migrations, 110; celestial navigation, 111; sea snake, 110, 134; turtle, 86, 110-111, 133-134, 171
Mimicry, phenomenon of, 86-88
Miskito Bank, Nicaragua, 171, *182*
Moccasins. *See* Copperhead; Cottonmouth
*Moloch horridus*, 27
Moloch lizards, 57
Monitor lizards, 13, 39, 83, 86, 112; komodo, 13, *14-15, 26,* 173-174; Nilotic, 114
Monk seal and turtle, 110
*Moschops*, *chart* 44, 47
Mosasaurs, 39, 112
Mound-nesting alligator, 131
Mouth: of alligator, *18;* snakes' distensibility of, 55, 57, *66*
Mud snake, 15
Mud turtle: common, *108;* striped, 131
Musk turtle, 106
Mutualism, 86
*Mystriosaurus* fossil, 50
Mythology, reptiles in, *146,* 147-149, 150-152

N aked-toed gecko, *98*
National Science Foundation, 171
*Natrix*, water snake, 114
Naval Research, Office of, 171
*Neoseps*, lizard, 83
Nesting: habits, 131, 143; migrations and grounds, 110-111, 133-134, 171, 173, 180, *183-185;* parental care, 132, 139, *142-143;* various nests, *131, 139,* 180
*Neusticurus rudis*, water lizard, 114
New Guinea, crocodile husbandry in, 174
New York, American Museum of Natural History, *34*
New York Zoological Society, 173
New Zealand tuatara. *See* Tuatara
Nile crocodile, *22,* 114, 151, 154; care of young, *142-143*
Norse mythology, snake in, 148
North American reptile populations, 11, 14, 15, 16, *map* 80, 131
*Nyctosaurus*, *46-47*

O live ridley, sea turtle, 134, *183*
*Opheodrys*, snake, 15
Orders, reptilian. *See* Classification
Orinoco River nesting grounds, 133
Ornithischians, *36,* 38, *chart* 44-45
Ostrich dinosaur, *40*
*Oxybelis*, vine snake, 86

P ainted turtle, *109*
Paleozoic, 37, 40, *chart* 44; time scales for, *chart* 37
Pancake turtles. *See* Soft-shelled turtles
Parasitism, 86
Parthenogenesis, 127

*Pelamis platurus*, sea snake, 114
Pelycosaurs, 40, *chart* 44-45
Peninsula cooter, nest of, *139*
Permian, 10, 38, 42, *chart* 44; time scales for, *chart* 37
Pets, reptiles as, 153; handling, *152-153*
Phytosaur, *41,* 42, 111
*Pictorial Museum of Animated Nature*, journal, 82, 150
Pine snake, *64-65*
Pit vipers, 15, 60. *See also* Rattlesnakes
*Placodus, 41;* skeleton, *48-49*
Plastron, of turtle shell, 10,156
Platynota, lizards, 112
Plesiosaurs, 42, *chart* 44-45, 48, 107, 108-109
Pleurodira, side-neck turtles, 11, 133
Pliny, 152
*Podocnemis*, turtle, 133
Poison: as defense device, 59, 60, 61-62; digestive function of, 61; as feeding device, 14, 59-61, 65, 69; makeup and effect of, 59, 61, 69, 70-71, 73
Poisonous lizards, 59
Poisonous snakes, 14-16, 56, 59-62, 65, *68-73,* 74, 154. *See also* Cobra; Rattlesnakes; Sea snakes; Vipers; etc.
Polynesian mythology, snake in, 148
Pond cooter, 128
Pope, Clifford, 13, 149-150
Predators, 76, 86; snakes as, 65
Proctor, John, 152
*Proganochelys*, *chart* 44
Protective devices and behavior, 157; camouflage by shape, 86; coloration, *60,* 61, 62, 86, 87-88, *92-93;* escape methods, *13, 158-161;* intimidation and bluffing, *60,* 61, *68-69,* 86, *158, 162-165;* mimicry, 86-88; poison, 59, 60, 61-62; rattle, *60,* 61-62; spiny scales, *166-167;* turtle shell, 10, 20
Protorosaurs, *chart* 44-45
*Pteranodon*, *chart* 44-45
Pterodactyls, 39-40
Pterosaurs, *38,* 39-40, 41, 44, *chart* 45, *46-47,* 83, 161
*Ptneopus garrulus*, gecko, 13
Puff adder, *158-159*
Pygmy rattlesnake, 16
Python, 14, 55, 154; African rock, 131; fertility related to size, 131; nesting behavior of Indian, 132, 139; pits of, 60; reticulate, 131; sizes of, 14, 25, *74-75;* vestigial legs of, 29

Q uetzalcoatl, god, 148

R acer, snake, 39, *75;* red, *90-91*
Racerunner, six-lined, 13
Rat snakes, 14, 54, 55; black, *75;* "combat" dance of, 129, 130
Rattlesnakes, 15, 63, 84, 99; in American heraldry, 152; in American Indian mythology, 148; charming of, 150; "combat" dance of, 130, *136;* fangs of, *72-73;* poisoning and trailing of prey by, 59, 60-61, 69; pygmy, 16; rattle of, *60,* 61-62, 87; size, 74. *See also* Diamondback rattler; Sidewinder
Recipes: iguana stew, 154; terrapin stew, 155

Red-bellied mud snake, 15
Red-bellied *Storeria*, 14
*Red Data Book* (IUCN), 172
"Red-eared" turtle, *109;* as pet, 153
Red racer, *90-91*
Religion, pervasion by reptiles, *146,* 147-149, 150-152
Reproduction: cases of parthenogenesis, 127; evolution of shelled egg and internal fertilization, 36-38, 141; fertility, 125, 131, 138-139; fertilization, 125, 126-127; forms of viviparous, 126. *See also* Egg, reptilian; Embryonic development; Live birth; Mating; Nesting
Reproductive organs, *18-19,* 126; paired copulatory of Squamata, 12, 126; tuatara, 175
*Rhamphorhynchus, 38, chart* 44-45
Rhynchocephalia, reptile order, 10, 16, 32, *chart* 44-45. *See also* Tuatara
Ribbon snake, 14
Ridley turtle, 110, 169, 173, *183; arribadas* of, 134, 173; species, 134
River turtles, South American, 133, 155
Romer, Alfred S., 37
Rubber boa, *163*

S almonellosis, 153
Salt gland, 107
Salt-marsh terrapin, 155
Salt-water crocodile, 16, 151, 154
Sand lizard, *90-91*
Sand-swimming, 83
Sand viper, 83
Sandfish, Australian, lizard, 83
Saurischians, *36,* 38, *chart* 44-45
Sauropods, 41
Sauropterygians, *chart* 44-45, *48-49*
Scales, 9, 35, 36, 40; of alligator, 18; function of, 85; of snakes and lizards, 12; spiny, for armor, *166-167*
Scarlet king snake, 88
Scarlet snake, 15, 88, *144-145*
Scincidae, lizard family, 13. *See also* Skinks
Scorpion lizard, 13
Scrub lizard, Florida, 80
Sea snakes, 113-114, 115, 117, *118-119;* black-and-yellow, 114; Japanese food consumption, 155; migrations of, 110, 134; poison of, 113; reproduction of, 113, 119, 134; salt gland of, 107
Sea turtles, *20-21,* 117; conservation efforts, 171-172, 180, *184-185;* courtship and mating of, 127, 128; decimation of populations, 134, 156, 171-173, *182;* delayed fertilization of, 126-127; exploitation for food, 155-156, 171, 180, *181-183;* locomotion of, 20, 96, 109; migrations of, 110-111, 134, 171; nesting habits, 119, *124,* 131, 134, 184; salt gland of, 107; shell of, 11, 20, 109, 155-156; sizes, 11, 106, 109. *See also* Green turtle; Hawksbill; Leatherback; Ridley
Sebek, god, 151, 152
*Seminatrix*, swamp snake, 114
Seminole Indians, 155
Sense organs: of alligator, *18-19;* Jacobson's organ, 12, 60-61, 98, 99; pit, 15, 60, 73; use in